Published in the UK in 2023
by Icon Books Ltd, Omnibus Business Centre,
39–41 North Road, London N7 9DP
info@iconbooks.com
www.iconbooks.com

sales@iconbooks.net

Distributed in the UK, Europe and Asia
by HarperCollins, Westerhill Rd, Bishopbriggs,
Glasgow G64 2QT

Distributed in South Africa
by Jonathan Ball, Office B4, The District,
41 Sir Lowry Road, Woodstock 7925

Distributed in India by Penguin Books India,
7th Floor, Infinity Tower-C, DLF Cyber City,
Gurgaon 122002, Haryana

Publisher: Jason Hook
Designer: Alex Coco
Illustrator: Robert Fiszer

ISBN: 978-1-83773-109-1

Printed in China

10 9 8 7 6 5 4 3 2 1

MATHS

Consultant Editor
KATIE STECKLES

Illustrations
ROBERT FISZER

ICON BOOKS

1 NUMBERS 8

2 STRUCTURES 28

3 LOGIC 46

4 GEOMETRY AND SHAPE 64

Mathematics is the language in which the scientific laws of the universe are written – from statistical analysis of experimental data to understanding the motion of physical bodies – and has many other applications, for example in problem solving and finance. Some parts of maths are studied by everyone at school, like basic numbers and geometry, but the subject is much bigger than that, with many different and interconnected areas, each with their own uses.

How can we understand such a hugely important and complex subject? We need a short cut, and this book will provide just that, guiding you to understand how mathematics underpins logical thinking, calculation and prediction, as well as being playful and beautiful.

We'll see how numbers go way beyond 1, 2, 3 and explore the mysteries of infinity, before considering some of the more abstract structures behind everything from social networks to Rubik's cubes. We can use basic logical thinking to solve problems, but mathematical logic has much more depth and can lead us to mind-bending paradoxes.

Alongside numbers and mathematical structures, we'll consider shapes: from simple objects to infinite patterns, and the ways geometry changes if we change the shape we're working on. We'll also talk about mathematical functions, and how they connect different branches of mathematics, and can be used in the study of fluid dynamics.

Mathematics gives us real power to study the world around us: statistics allows us to collect small amounts of data and use it to generalise findings to much larger populations, while mathematical modelling lets us understand and predict the behaviour of complicated systems. We'll see how probability helps us understand if the observations we're making are really meaningful, and why mathematical models are only an approximation of reality, but powerful nonetheless.

All of this serious, useful maths is important, but maths is also a great tool for play – we'll find out about how the ancient Egyptians used recreational maths puzzles for fun, and how maths gives us tools to analyse strategy and win at games – whether they're fun competitions between friends, or the larger-scale activities of international politics.

While this is only a small slice of the many wonderful applications and tools mathematicians have at their disposal, this book will take you on a journey to see what's out there and what's possible, using the power of mathematical thinking.

Enjoy the ride!

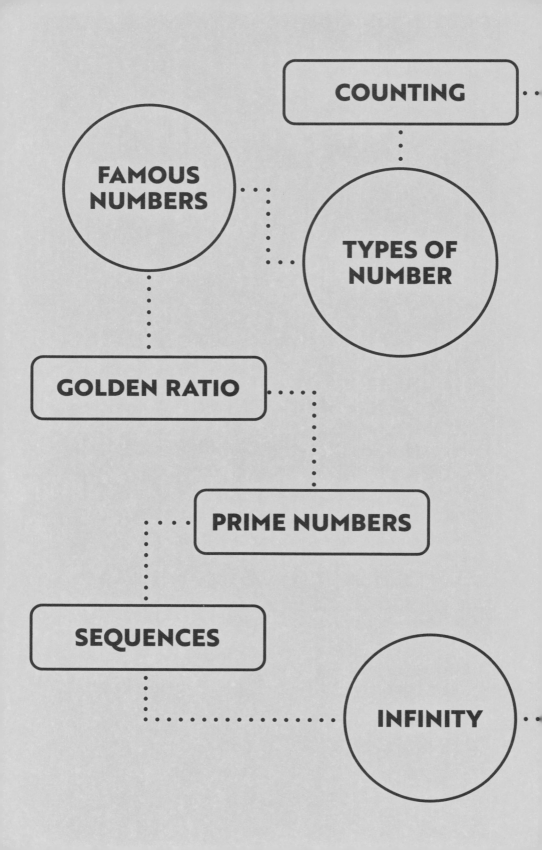

CHAPTER 1

NUMBERS

IMAGINARY NUMBERS

COMPLEX NUMBERS

INTRODUCTION

When people think of mathematics, they most often think about numbers: the universal notion of quantity underpins much of mathematical thinking, and most people's experience with mathematics revolves around arithmetic, counting and quantity. While there are plenty of other kinds of mathematics – as you'll see elsewhere in this book – numbers are a fundamental part of maths.

From the basic principles of **COUNTING** – using your fingers, tally marks or more complicated systems – humans have been enumerating and quantifying the world around them for over 40,000 years. Being able to convert a collection of objects in the real world to a numerical value allows us to apply ideas from mathematics to real situations. Even though it's a skill learned in early childhood, counting underpins much of our understanding of the world.

In order to count, you need numbers. While most counting relies on plain old **WHOLE NUMBERS**, mathematicians have taken this starting point and played with it to produce other types of number – **FRACTIONS**, decimals, the exotic **IRRATIONAL NUMBERS** and even imaginary numbers, which lead us on to **COMPLEX NUMBERS**.

Some numbers are so useful and important they've achieved celebrity status. Famous numbers like the circle constant, π **(PI)**, and the square root of 2, have important roles in mathematics. They interact in intriguing ways, and crop up in unexpected places. Another example is the golden ratio, ϕ **(PHI)**, which has many interesting properties and is visible in elegant ratios and beautiful rectangles.

Numbers are so interesting, there's a whole branch of mathematics dedicated to them: number theory is the study of the properties and relationships of numbers, in particular positive whole numbers, or **NATURAL NUMBERS**. One special category is **PRIME NUMBERS**, which have only two **FACTORS** – 1 and the number itself. Numbers like 8 or 15 can be broken down into smaller chunks, but the primes are indivisible and form the building blocks of all numbers.

Once you've got your head around numbers themselves, you can construct **SEQUENCES**: lists of numbers which follow a particular rule or pattern. Arithmetic sequences have a fixed gap between each term (e.g., 5, 10, 15, 20 ...). In some sequences, called **GEOMETRIC SEQUENCES**, each term is a fixed multiple of the previous one (e.g., 1, 2, 4, 8, 16, 32 ...), leading to exponential growth. We'll see how this idea can be linked to musical notes and the patterns behind harmony.

While mathematicians wouldn't necessarily categorise it as a number, no discussion of counting and numerical sequences would be complete without a mention of **INFINITY** – the tantalising but unreachable endpoint of the number line. As well as considering the magnitude of the infinite set of all possible numbers, we'll see how mathematicians have identified different sizes of infinity and make a visit to David Hilbert's metaphorical infinite hotel.

Exploring the different types of numbers (finite and otherwise) used in mathematics – and in engineering, physics and computer science – will reveal it's really not as easy as 1, 2, 3.

NUMBERS MAP

NUMBERS

NUMBERS

A number is a general representation of many specific examples; the number 7 could represent the length of a piece of wood, the people in a family, or the sides of a shape. Representing things as numbers allows us to make connections and spot patterns in areas that seem totally unrelated.

COMPLEX NUMBERS

Using the square root of −1 as a basis, complex numbers extend numbers into a 2D plane. They have many uses in engineering and pure maths.

WHOLE NUMBERS/ NATURAL NUMBERS

The counting numbers: 0, 1, 2, 3, ...

INTEGERS

The counting numbers and their negative counterparts: ... −3, −2, −1, 0, 1, 2, 3 ...

RATIONAL NUMBERS/ FRACTIONS

Numbers that can be made by dividing one integer by another.

SEQUENCES

A sequence is a list of numbers generated by a rule. We can study the patterns in sequences of numbers, and the structures they represent.

FACTORS

A number that can be divided exactly into another number, with nothing left over.

INFINITY

Not considered to be a number, infinity is the size of something which goes on forever; it can be different sizes.

GEOMETRIC SEQUENCE

A sequence in which each term is in a fixed ratio to the previous one – such as the frequencies of musical notes.

COUNTING

COUNTING

Counting is the process of assigning a number to each object in a group, in order to find out how many there are. It's the most fundamental concept from which the rest of mathematics has grown.

FINGER COUNTING

A system of counting that uses fingers to keep track of a total. Different methods of finger counting have arisen in cultures around the world.

RATIO

A relationship between two quantities that defines how many times larger one is than the other.

IRRATIONAL NUMBERS

Numbers that cannot be made by dividing one integer by another. Examples of irrational numbers include $\sqrt{2}$ and π.

PRIME NUMBERS

Numbers with no exact factors. They are the building blocks of numbers and are important in number theory; they also have uses in cryptography.

FAMOUS NUMBERS

Numbers that are so ubiquitous and useful that they crop up in many different areas of maths. They've achieved celebrity status, even among non-mathematicians.

ϕ (PHI)

The 'Golden Ratio' is the unique number found when the ratio of two numbers a and b is equal to the ratio of the sum of the numbers to the larger of the numbers: $a/b = (a+b)/a = \phi$.

π (PI)

The ratio of a circle's circumference to its diameter, known as the 'circle constant'.

How high can you count on your fingers?

⟶ **Higher than you might think! The obvious answer is 10, with each finger (including the thumbs) representing one counting number. But with some imaginative counting methods you can go as high as 1,023.**

Counting seems to be an almost fundamental part of being human. Counting on your fingers leaves no archaeological trace, but there is evidence from at least 40,000 years ago showing ancient societies using tally marks, including the Lebombo bone, a 42,000-year-old piece of baboon's fibula. It was discovered in Swaziland in the 1970s and has 29 notches cut into it. If ancient humans could mark tallies on a bone, it seems likely that they would also have counted on their fingers.

The most basic method of finger counting uses one digit for each counting number. Most people have 10 digits, which leads to a natural predisposition to a base-10 counting system. This is why we have 10 different number symbols, and is also why the word 'digit' can mean either a finger or a numeral below 10. A symbol's position within a number corresponds to a power of 10: 1, 10, 100, 1,000, and so on. But once you've counted your 10 fingers, the only way to go higher is to use some other method to keep track of how many 10s you've counted.

One method for counting higher than 10 is to use the thumb to count each of the three segments of each finger separately, giving a count of 12 on each hand. If you use one hand to keep track of how many times you've counted 12 on the other, you can count as high as 156 (13 groups of 12, including the one where the thumb of the second hand isn't pointing at anything). That's a good improvement on 10.

But you can do better than that! You could use your fingers to represent a binary number, with each finger indicating a 1 if it's held up and a 0 if it isn't. Binary is a base-2 counting system, which means that each digit represents a power of 2: 1, 2, 4, 8, and so on. The highest number you can make with 10 digits is 1,023, which is an impressive total for just 10 fingers!

FINGER COUNTING

In the first pair of hands, the first hand shows a count of 8, and the second hand shows a count of 4 × 12 = 48. The total count is 48 + 8 = 56. The second pair of hands shows the binary number 1010110011. As a decimal number, this is 1 + 2 + 16 + 32 + 128 + 512 = 691.

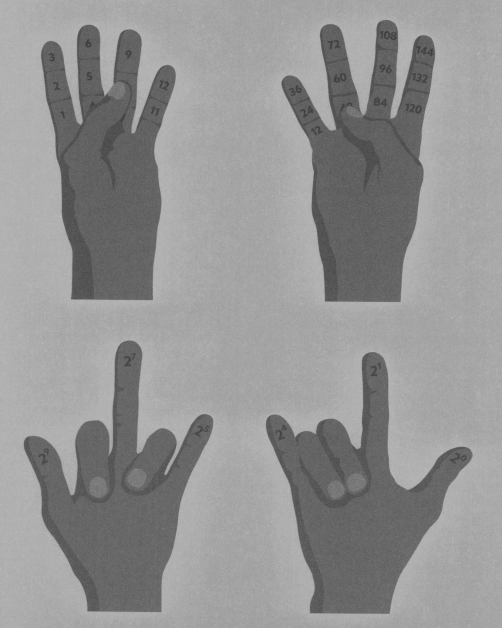

What's so 'golden' about the golden ratio?

⟶ **The golden ratio is an irrational number, approximately 1.618, usually represented by the Greek letter ϕ (phi). The 'golden' in the name refers to its beauty, the idea that it is the best ratio aesthetically.**

When people talk about the beauty of the golden ratio, they often mention that it appears in nature – in the spirals of a pine cone, for example. Or they might mention its use in the proportions of famous paintings. But ϕ has a fundamental beauty that goes deeper than how it is used. Mathematically, the golden ratio defines a relationship between two numbers a and b, where a is larger than b. If the ratio of a to b (a divided by b) is the same as the ratio of $a + b$ to a ($a + b$ divided by a) then that ratio must be 1.618, or ϕ.

It might not be immediately obvious why this relationship is beautiful. Imagine you have a rectangle where the ratio of the longer side to the shorter side is ϕ. If you cut off a square with sides the length of the shorter side of the rectangle, you'll be left with a smaller rectangle where the ratio of the longer side to the shorter side is also ϕ. What's more,

if you repeat this process on the new rectangle, you'll be left with an even smaller rectangle whose sides are also in the ratio of ϕ. You can continue the process, making smaller and smaller rectangles, but however small you go you'll always be left with a rectangle whose side lengths are in the same ratio. Mathematicians often see beauty in simply defined relationships with interesting properties, and ϕ definitely satisfies those criteria.

ϕ isn't the only famous mathematical number. Another ratio that can be simply defined but that has far-reaching effects throughout mathematics is pi, or π, which is approximately 3.14 and is the ratio of the circumference of a circle to its diameter. Any circle, no matter how big or small, will have its circumference and diameter in this ratio. The fact that this one number can describe any circle gives π a distinct beauty of its own.

PAPER SIZES

Like φ (bottom), the square root of 2 is an irrational number that is interesting as a ratio. If you have a rectangle where the ratio of the long side to the short side is the square root of 2, and you cut it in half, both new rectangles will have sides in the same ratio as the original one. This is how UK paper sizes work: in A4 paper, the ratio of the long side to the short side is the square root of 2, and the same is true for A5, A6, and so on.

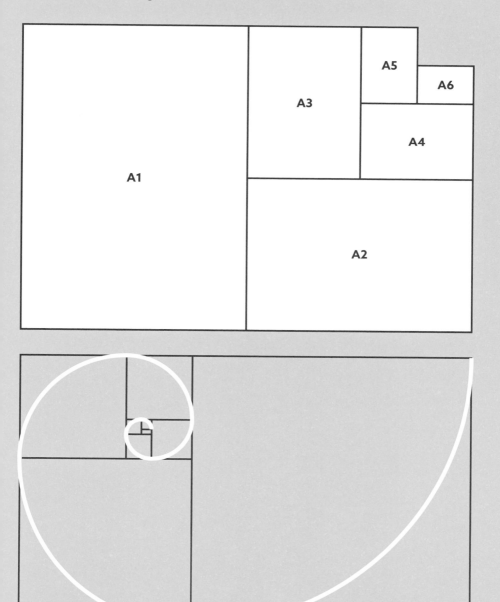

How many types of number are there?

⟶ You may as well ask how many numbers there are! Mathematicians have a standard way to classify numbers, but within those sets you can probably define as many different types of number as there are numbers themselves.

The natural numbers are the counting numbers: 0, 1, 2, 3, ... Add or multiply two natural numbers and you'll get another natural number.

If you subtract a natural number from a smaller natural number, you get a number below zero: a negative number. The integers include all the natural numbers and all their negative counterparts: ..., −3, −2, −1, 0, 1, 2, 3, ... Now you can subtract to your heart's content.

What if you divide an integer by an integer? Unless one is a multiple of the other, you'll get a fraction. The rational numbers are all the numbers that can be written as a fraction of two integers. This includes all the integers, as any integer n can be written as the fraction $n/1$.

How about when you take the square root of a positive rational number? Sometimes you'll get another rational number (the square root of 4 is 2). Sometimes you'll get an irrational number, with a decimal part that goes on forever without repeating: the square root of 2 is 1.414213562....

There are also irrational numbers that are not square roots, such as the famous constants π and ϕ (see page 12). The set of real numbers includes all rational and irrational numbers.

To find the square root of a negative number you'll need a new number, i, which is defined as the square root of −1. You can write the square root of any negative number as i multiplied by the square root of its positive counterpart. These are all imaginary numbers.

If you add an imaginary number to a real number you'll get a complex number. The set of complex numbers includes all real and imaginary numbers, because any real number r can be written as $r + 0i$, and any imaginary number can be written as 0 + a multiple of i.

Within these sets, you can define other types of number. A prime number is a natural number with exactly two factors (see page 20). An algebraic number is a complex number that is a solution to a polynomial equation. The number of types of number is limited only by your imagination.

THE NUMBER SETS

The main number sets all fit one inside another, so the complex numbers contain the real numbers, which contain the rational numbers, which contain the integers, which contain the natural numbers. Within those sets you can define other sets. For example, the set of prime numbers is a subset of the natural numbers, which means that every prime number is also a natural number, and the set of fractions with even denominators is a subset of the rational numbers.

Complex numbers

Real numbers

Rational numbers

Integers

Natural numbers

$\frac{2}{9}+23i$

$\sqrt{59}$

$\frac{4}{5}$

-1

$\sqrt{2}$

8

2 3 9

$\frac{36}{47}$

$\frac{7}{16}$

-3

-2

ϕ

Fractions with an even denominator

π

$-2i$

i

Prime numbers

$7+2i$

Imaginary numbers

Multiples of 3

What's the next prime number?

⟶ **Nobody knows! Although mathematicians have studied prime numbers for thousands of years, there is no reliable formula to generate prime numbers or to predict the next one.**

A prime number is a number with exactly two factors: one and itself. They start with 2, 3, 5, 7, 11, and so on. Evidence has been found that humans have known of prime numbers since ancient Egyptian times, c.1550 BCE, but the first person known to study prime numbers was the Greek mathematician Euclid, c.300 BCE. Euclid proved that there are an infinite number of primes. As well as the study of prime numbers being a fascinating subject in itself, large prime numbers are essential for modern computer security.

The ancient Greek mathematician Eratosthenes created an algorithm for finding all prime numbers up to a chosen maximum. Called the Sieve of Eratosthenes, it's an efficient and systematic way of finding all the primes within a given list of numbers. Unfortunately, it becomes impractical as your list gets longer.

The prime numbers seem to be deeply random, and this can be seen by studying their frequency. A 'prime gap' is the difference between two consecutive prime numbers. The smallest, and only odd, prime gap is the gap of 1 between 2 and 3, while the largest currently known is 1,113,106, between two primes with over 18,000 digits. The prime number theorem tells us that primes become less common as numbers get larger, and yet the twin prime conjecture claims that there are infinitely many prime gaps of size 2. This conjecture has not yet been proved, but the evidence is so strong that most mathematicians believe it is almost certain to be true.

The Great Internet Mersenne Prime Search (GIMPS) is a collaborative project that uses crowd-sourced computing power to search for large prime numbers. A Mersenne prime is a prime number that is one less than a prime power of 2. For example, if $p = 2$ then $2^p - 1 = 3$, and since both 2 and 3 are prime this means that 3 is a Mersenne prime. The largest known prime as of 2023 was found by GIMPS and has nearly 25 million digits. Nobody knows what the next one will be.

THE SIEVE OF ERATOSTHENES

The Sieve of Eratosthenes is an ancient algorithm for finding prime numbers. Start with a list of all the numbers from 2 up to your chosen maximum. The first prime is 2; circle it and cross out all its multiples. The smallest number that hasn't been crossed out will be the next prime number (in this case, 3). Circle this, then cross out all its multiples. Keep going until all the numbers in your list have been either circled or crossed out – the circled numbers will be all the primes in your list.

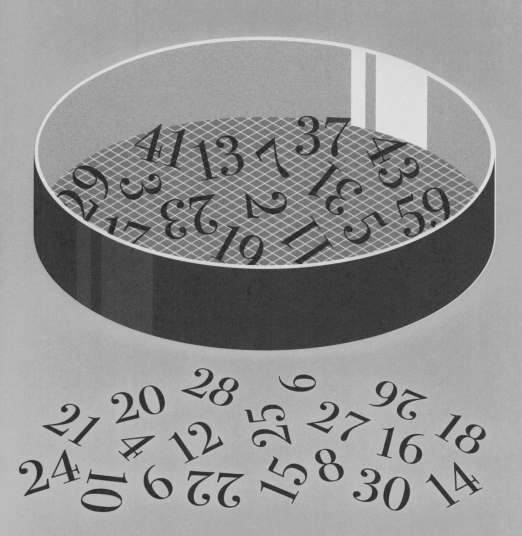

When is a perfect fifth not a perfect fifth?

⟶ **Pythagoras defined a perfect fifth as the difference in pitch between two plucked strings whose lengths are in the ratio 2 : 3. But most modern Western music uses a tuning system called equal temperament, in which the ratio is slightly different.**

The pitch of any note you hear depends on the frequency of the vibrations causing the sound signal, where the frequency is the number of vibrations per second, measured in Hz. This is a numerical quantity that can be studied mathematically. An interval is the difference in pitch between two notes and can be measured by the ratio of their frequencies. If the frequencies are in the ratio 1 : 2, the two notes will be an octave apart (e.g., middle C and the next C up).

The idea of an octave is fundamental to all known musical systems throughout the world, but there are many different ways to tune the notes within an octave. The most common tuning system in Western music is equal temperament, which uses a geometric sequence to define the frequency of each note.

In a geometric sequence, you multiply each term by a fixed number to get the next term. For example, in the sequence 1, 2, 4, 8, 16, each term is the previous term multiplied by 2. To get from the first term, 1, to the fifth term, 16, you multiply by 2 four times: $1 \times 2^4 = 16$. To apply this idea to music theory, start with the premise that any pair of notes an octave apart should have a ratio of 1 : 2. The starting note is the first term in the sequence, and there are 12 notes in the musical scale, so the note an octave above will be the 13th term. We need a number that, when multiplied by itself 12 times, gives 2. This number is the twelfth root of 2, or approximately 1.05946.

How much of a difference does this make to the pitch? Well, the A above middle C has a frequency of 440 Hz. A perfect fifth above A is E (seven notes above A). Using Pythagoras' ratio of 2 : 3, the frequency of E is 660 Hz. Using equal temperament its frequency is approximately $440 \times 1.05946^7 = 659.2416$ Hz. That's pretty close – but not perfect!

PERFECT FIFTHS AND OCTAVES

A perfect fifth is seven notes above the original note, and an octave is 12 notes above, so moving up by 12 perfect fifths should be the same as moving up by seven octaves. But 12 perfect fifths is a ratio of $2^{12} : 3^{12} = 4,096 : 531,441$ (or $1 : 129.746$) and seven octaves is a ratio of $1^7 : 2^7 = 1 : 128$. *They're close, but they're not the same! Different tuning systems adjust for this difference in different ways, one of which is the equal temperament system, which divides an octave (or other musical interval) into equal steps.*

How can some infinities be larger than others?

→ The idea of infinity means to go on forever, so you would think that nothing can be bigger than infinity. But in the 19th century, a mathematician proved that one infinite set of numbers can be bigger than another.

Infinity is difficult to comprehend, so let's start with something finite. The set of numbers 1, 2, 3, 4, 5 is finite – it contains five numbers. The set of natural numbers (see page 18) from one to a million is much bigger, but it's still finite – it contains one million numbers. The set of all natural numbers, however, is infinite – however large a number you reach, you can always add one more.

A set of numbers is called *countably infinite* if every number in it can be mapped to one of the natural numbers. So any countably infinite set is the same size as the set of natural numbers. For example, the set of integers is countable. This feels paradoxical – every natural number (except 0) can be mapped to two integers, itself and its negative self, so the integers must be twice as big. But there is a way to systematically pair every integer with exactly one natural number. Start by pairing zero with zero. Then pair each positive number in the integers with its double in the natural

numbers, so 1 is paired with 2, 2 with 4, and so on. This leaves all the odd natural numbers to be paired with the negative integers – there are no integers left over and so the two sets are the same size.

An *uncountably infinite* set cannot be mapped to the set of natural numbers without having some members left over. The set of real numbers is one example. Irrational numbers – numbers with an infinite number of decimal places and no repeating pattern – are included in the real numbers, and the systematic approach doesn't work for these numbers. Georg Cantor, a 19th-century mathematician, showed that for any mapping of the real numbers to the natural numbers, there would always be a way to construct a new real number that was different from every real number that had already been included. Since all the natural numbers were already mapped to a real number, this new real number couldn't have a partner. This showed that the real numbers are a bigger infinity than the natural numbers.

HILBERT'S HOTEL

Hilbert's Hotel, in a thought experiment created in 1924 by mathematician David Hilbert, has an infinite number of rooms, all of which are occupied. But when a new guest turns up, rather than turning them away, you can ask each guest to move to the room numbered one greater than the room they're in, leaving Room 1 for the new guest. A similar trick can be used for any countably infinite number of new guests – but if an uncountably infinite busload of guests turns up, some of them will be left without a room.

Do imaginary numbers really exist?

→ The first imaginary number was defined as the solution to an equation that didn't have any solutions in the then-known number systems. But imaginary numbers are now used in many real-world applications, so we can say that they do exist – though what 'exists' means is a whole other philosophical question!

Think of a number that you can square to get an answer of 1. It could be 1, because 1^2 is equal to 1, or it could be −1, because $(-1)^2$ is also equal to 1. Now think of a number that you can square to get an answer of −1. We already know that it can't be 1 or −1, because both of those give an answer of 1 when squared. So how can we solve this puzzle?

That's where imaginary numbers come in. The imaginary unit, i, is defined as the number that you square to get −1. This immediately makes it a solution to our puzzle. This feels like a trick – rather than solving the puzzle, or admitting that it can't be solved, we've simply invented a new number and called it a solution. And a few hundred years ago, many mathematicians would have agreed with this point of view. The very name 'imaginary', first used by René Descartes in the 17th century, was intended as an insult, implying that imaginary numbers can no more be said to exist than, say, a unicorn.

Imaginary numbers and complex numbers – numbers with both a real part and an imaginary part – are essential in many fields of science, engineering and the arts. They can be used to calculate electromagnetic current, to analyse and filter an audio recording, to describe a quantum waveform and to generate realistic computer graphics. So you may not be able to recognise an imaginary number in the real world in the same way that you could recognise that you have '12' of something, but they are used to describe and analyse phenomena that are occurring all around you, and in that sense they really do exist.

COMPLEX NUMBERS

A complex number is a number with a real part and an imaginary part. For example, the complex number 6 + 4i has a real part of 6 and an imaginary part of 4. Complex numbers can be plotted on a coordinate grid, called the complex plane, by using the real part as the x coordinate and the imaginary part as the y coordinate. This makes complex numbers, and their four-dimensional counterparts, quaternions, useful in computer graphics – they allow movements such as rotations to be calculated as additions and multiplications that are easier to program and more efficient than other methods.

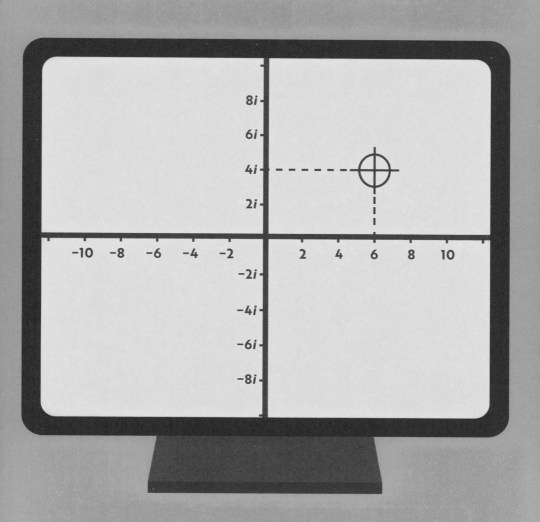

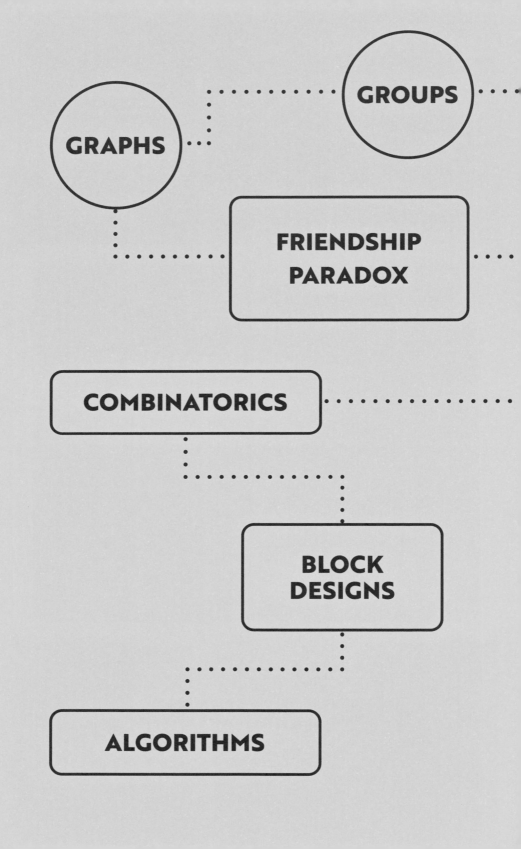

CHAPTER 2

STRUCTURES

VECTOR
SPACES

INTRODUCTION

Mathematics is seen by many as being a cold, logical and **ABSTRACT** subject. While it's certainly not cold, there is some truth in the 'logical' and 'abstract' parts. And one of the great strengths of being abstract is that you can strip away any messy, real-world complications to find the underlying structure of something, allowing you to study it in a purer form.

This also means that you can apply tools you've developed elsewhere by studying the same abstract ideas in different contexts, and generalising the ideas to previously unconsidered cases. Surprisingly often, maths is about creative thinking and play, and the sandbox of abstraction allows for imaginary worlds filled with lots of possibilities.

In this chapter, we'll travel through these imaginary worlds to visit some of the most common mathematical abstractions. Some of the **STRUCTURES** you encounter may be familiar to you already. The numbers and shapes you studied in school, for example, provide examples of mathematical **GROUPS**. Mathematicians also make use of arrangements of dots and lines, like a dot-to-dot puzzle, to model network structures and more abstract ideas using **GRAPHS**.

Other types of structure are more complex. **VECTORS**, which can be thought of as arrows in 2D or 3D space that point in a direction with a given length, can be used to model moving gases and liquids, magnetic fields and gradients, and in computer graphics. We can also mathematically describe the number of different ways to combine and rearrange objects by using **COMBINATORICS**. This can lead to some insightful discoveries about the complexity of seemingly simple systems, and help to make scientific experiments more effective. Meanwhile, understanding the mathematical structure behind **ALGORITHMS** can allow us to program computers so that they achieve incredible feats.

Mathematicians are big fans of structure, since it provides order in the face of a potentially complicated problem or situation, allowing us to categorise and find similarities in disparate areas of study. Many major mathematical discoveries have been based on the serendipity of someone noticing a shared structure between two seemingly unrelated objects, and uncovering a previously unknown link across different branches of mathematics.

Structure also gives us a shared language, independent of context. Mathematical ideas have been discovered in many different parts of the world across the centuries. The notation used to describe them is mostly the same, no matter where you're from or what language you speak, and concepts originating from ancient cultures and historical thinkers from all over the world are still understood and employed today.

In this chapter, while we'll visit only a few of the many different types of structure used and studied by mathematicians, we will also discover connections to many of the other areas within maths that are covered in this book.

STRUCTURES MAP

GROUPS

GROUP
An algebraic structure consisting of a set with an identity element, inverses and a well-defined binary operation.

ALGEBRAIC STRUCTURE
An abstract structure consisting of an underlying set, along with rules about how to combine the objects from the set.

IDENTITY ELEMENT
A unique element of a group that has no effect when combined with other elements.

INVERSES
Elements of a group which cancel out when combined.

ABSTRACTION
The process of modelling a real-world or complex system using a pure mathematical structure.

FRIENDSHIP PARADOX
A consequence of graph structure meaning your friends have more friends than you do.

GRAPH
A network of points joined by lines.

VECTORS

VECTOR SPACE

A structure containing vectors, which can be combined by addition or scaled using numbers.

VECTOR FIELD

A space with a vector attached at each point, which can be used to describe air flow or magnetic fields.

COMPLEXITY

A measure of how difficult or time-consuming algorithms are to implement.

ALGORITHM

A set of instructions a computer or human can follow to complete a task.

BLOCK DESIGN

A particular type of combinatorial structure concerned with arranging objects into blocks.

PROJECTIVE PLANES

Geometric interpretations of block design structures.

COMBINATORICS

The study of counting the ways to combine and rearrange things.

COMBINATIONS AND PERMUTATIONS

Ways of enumerating choices and orderings of a given set of objects.

How do you solve a Rubik's cube?

⟶ **While it's an object many think of as a children's toy, the Rubik's cube has an incredibly complex underlying structure which can be described mathematically – and in order to solve it, we can use the language of groups.**

The underlying mathematical structure here is a group – a set of objects which can be combined in pairs, giving another object also found in the same set. For example, whole numbers combined using addition form a group, as any two whole numbers added together give another whole number.

With a couple of additional conditions to make sure combining behaves sensibly, we find that groups have a few key properties. There's always an object in the group which corresponds to doing nothing, called the identity element. If you combine an element with the identity element, you'll get the same element back. In numbers with addition, the identity element is zero, as adding zero does nothing.

Each element also has a unique inverse element. If you combine an element with its inverse, you'll get the identity element. In the case of whole numbers, each number's inverse is the corresponding negative number: for example, $4 + (-4) = 0$.

The classic 1970s twisty puzzle, made from a cube divided into a 3-by-3-by-3 arrangement of smaller 'cubies', has an incredible number of possible configurations – around 43 billion billion. These configurations can be thought of as sequences of twists: the moves you need to perform on a solved cube to get to this state.

Since any two sequences of twists performed one after the other will result in a new configuration, the set of moves on the Rubik's cube forms a group – it's such a classic example, the page about groups on Wikipedia is illustrated with a picture of the Rubik's cube. The identity element in this case is the 'move' consisting of not doing anything (sitting and admiring your solved cube), and the inverse of a move is that move performed backwards – with the twists made in the opposite direction, in reverse order.

Applying a move and then its inverse to the Rubik's cube will return the cube to the configuration you started with. So, to solve a scrambled cube you need to determine which of the 43 billion billion possible combinations of moves have been applied to it to make it scrambled, then work out the inverse of that and apply it to the cube. Simple!

GROUPS

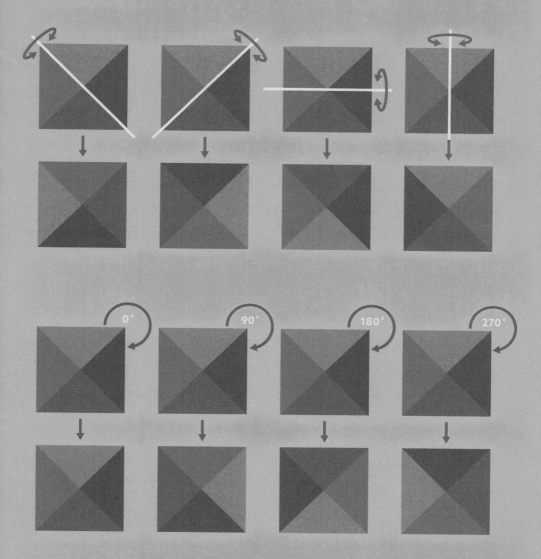

There are many examples of group structures, including the Rubik's cube, the 12 numbers on a clock face, and the rotations and reflections of a square, as shown here. Every group contains an identity element (which corresponds with an unchanged state), and each element has a uniquely defined inverse. Mathematicians study groups as they allow us to interpret and describe the behaviour of numbers, shapes, symmetries and more complex abstract structures.

Why do all my friends have more friends than I do?

——➤ With social networking, it's easy to count the number of friends you have and compare it to others. Due to a mathematical result called the friendship paradox, people will on average tend to have fewer friends than their friends do.

⇗ Don't worry; it's nothing personal – different people have different numbers of friends, and the phenomenon occurs because people with more friends are more likely to be in your friend group (since their own friend group is larger). People with fewer friends are statistically less likely to be connected to you. Overall, this means that for a randomly chosen person it's more likely their friends are better connected than they are.

The mathematical analysis of this kind of problem uses an area of maths called graph theory – the study of networks, called graphs, consisting of nodes (points) and edges (lines between a pair of points). Since the graph is purely recording the way things are connected together, the precise geometry of the lines and nodes on the page isn't important. Graphs can be used to model all kinds of situations and systems, including social networks, and we know many useful tools and results about graphs which we can apply to these contexts.

One useful tool is graph colouring – the nodes of a graph can each be assigned a colour so that any two nodes which are connected by an edge are different colours. For a given graph, the chromatic number is the smallest number of colours needed to properly colour the graph, and this can range from 2 (for a class of graphs called bipartite) up to a value one more than the largest number of edges attached to any one node in the graph.

Graphs can also be studied in terms of how they're connected – for example, could you draw it with one line without taking your pen off the paper and finishing back where you started (an Eulerian graph)? This could be useful for working out an efficient parcel delivery route. Could you draw it with no edges crossing (a planar graph)? This becomes important in designing layouts of wires on a circuit board.

REAL-WORLD NETWORKS

Different types of graph can be used to model real-world networks. In a weighted graph, we assign a numerical value to each edge – for example, to show distances and model a road network. In a directed graph, we use directional arrows on edges to indicate one-way relationships – for example, to show friend connections.

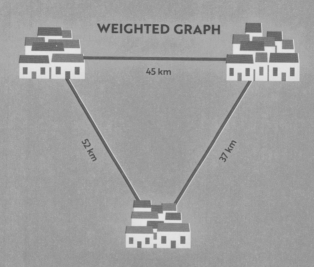

WEIGHTED GRAPH

45 km

52 km

37 km

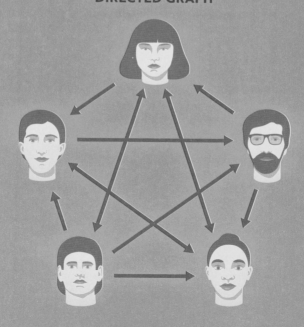

DIRECTED GRAPH

Why can't you comb a hairy ball?

→ Imagine a ball entirely covered in short hair that you're combing to make it lie flat. No matter what you try, there's always a bit that sticks up somewhere. This is explained by a mathematical theorem called the hairy ball theorem!

The hairs on the ball can be thought of as vectors – arrows, attached at each point of the surface of the ball, which can point in any direction. The way real hairs lie on top of each other is a good model for the way mathematicians like collections of vectors, called vector fields, to behave – the individual vectors can't pass through each other, and they tend to point in a similar direction to the ones around them.

The hairy ball theorem says that for any well-behaved vector field like this on the surface of a sphere, there's no way to comb all the hairs so they all lie flat – there will always be at least one point where some hairs stick straight up. This is a consequence of the geometry of a sphere – if we were combing hairs on a flat square, or on a shape with a different geometry, like the surface of a torus (doughnut), we could comb them all flat without any problems But a sphere has the right curvature to make this impossible.

Vector fields can be used to model real-world systems like air currents – the vectors point in the direction the wind is blowing at each point on the surface of the earth. A neat consequence of the theorem is that at any time, there must be at least one place on the surface of the planet where there's no horizontal wind current.

VECTOR FIELDS

The mathematical concept of vector fields allows us to model real-world situations like air flow and magnetic fields – and even the hair on a person's head. Hairdressers know all too well that anyone with short hair (and a standard spherical head) will have a cowlick on the back of the skull, where the hair sticks out awkwardly and won't be combed flat. Mathematics tells us this will always happen!

How many ways are there to shuffle a deck of cards?

⟶ While it might seem like a simple object, a standard deck of 52 playing cards has an incredibly large number of possible orders it can be shuffled into – 80,658,175, 170,943,878,571,660,636,856,403,766,975,289, 505,440,883,277,824,000,000,000,000 to be exact.

Calculating these kinds of numbers – that describe the number of different orderings a set of objects can have – is part of a branch of maths called combinatorics. A reshuffling of a set of objects is called a permutation, and the number of possible permutations for a given number of objects is a well-known quantity.

Imagine we had a deck of just five cards, and consider it one card at a time – there are five choices for the card on the bottom of the pile. But once we've chosen a bottom card, there are four cards we could choose to put on top of that, then three cards, then two, and then one card left which has to go on top. This means we have $5 \times 4 \times 3 \times 2 \times 1$ different possible orderings for the deck – a total of 120 different possibilities.

We call this calculation a factorial, and it's denoted using an exclamation mark:

$5! = 5 \times 4 \times 3 \times 2 \times 1 = 120$. The value of $n!$ tells us how many ways we can order n things: so for 52 cards, it's 52! – an epic multiplication of $52 \times 51 \times 50 \times ... \times 2 \times 1$ which gives the monstrous total above. This is an incredibly large number – it's around a billion billion times the number of atoms making up the earth and everything on it.

We can also use this to calculate the number of possible 5-card hands. We have 52 choices for the first card, 51 for the second, and so on – stopping at 48 choices for the fifth card, giving 311,875,200 possibilities. But this will include all hands that contain these five cards, including if we'd drawn them in a different order – so we need to divide by the number of ways to order five cards – our 120 above – giving a more reasonable 2,598,960 possible 5-card hands.

COMBINATORICS

Combinatorics is an area of mathematics concerned with the arrangement of objects in a set. These kinds of calculations can be used to inform probability when playing card games – to calculate the chances of the cards you need being dealt to you in a poker game, or work out the odds of a risky gamble paying off. Combinatorics also has more serious applications in statistical and quantum physics, evolutionary biology and computer science.

How can maths help to design a good medical experiment?

⟶ Medical experiments often involve testing different treatments on different groups, and they need to be carefully arranged to ensure fairness and scientific accuracy. Design theory, a branch of combinatorics, allows us to cleverly arrange things in groups and has some useful applications.

Design theory centres around the idea of block designs: sets of successive arrangements of objects into groups, so that each object gets to be in a group with each other object a certain number of times.

A simple example would be 15 golfers planning a week away. There are seven days of golf games to plan, and the golfers will play in groups of three each day. But the golfers don't want to end up playing against the same opponent more than once – can we arrange the games so nobody has to do that?

This problem was originally posed as a puzzle in 1850, and there are exactly seven possible ways to solve it. This is an example of a type of block design called a Steiner system, and such systems can be designed to meet a variety of constraints – in this case, we want any two players to appear together in exactly one game, but we could instead require that any three golfers only play together exactly once, and we can vary the number of golfers, the number of games and the number of players in each game.

There are some configurations where no solution is possible, but block design theory allows us to find combinations when they do work, and this has useful applications in the design of medical experiments. Allocating participants randomly to different groups within a study might result in unanticipated imbalances in the experiment, skewing the results. Block designs allow trials to be arranged so that the effect of having participants with similar conditions or backgrounds won't impact on the accuracy of the results.

BLOCK DESIGNS

Block designs help us symmetrically sort objects into groups. Six golfers can be arranged into three pairs for five games – but if we tried to add a sixth day to the tournament, we'd be forced to repeat a pair we'd already seen. Block designs also have applications in tournament scheduling and designing lotteries, as well as in the design of algorithms (see page 44), networking and cryptography. They're also related to magic squares – arrangements of numbers where each row and column has the same sum.

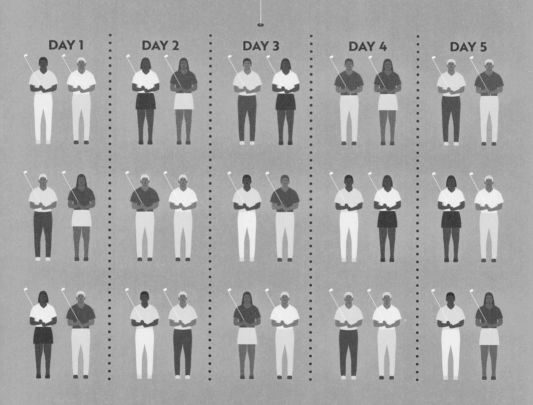

DAY 1　　DAY 2　　DAY 3　　DAY 4　　DAY 5

Why is a computer like an amateur chef?

⟶ **Even though computers can be incredibly powerful and make billions of calculations per second, they're limited in that they can only follow the instructions they're given – much like someone following a recipe.**

Computer programs, along with a lot of common techniques in mathematics, are based on algorithms. These are sequences of instructions which can be followed to produce a result. You might be familiar with long division from school – this is a set of steps you follow to take the input numbers and produce an output, and many other mathematical algorithms follow the same idea.

There are mathematical algorithms for many common procedures – finding common divisors or factors of numbers, manipulating matrices or grids of numbers, or calculating square roots. There's even a mathematical algorithm for fitting a collection of boxes into a given space efficiently. And all of these can easily be implemented by computers, since they can be written as sets of instructions with inputs and outputs.

Since computers can only interpret the instructions they're given, a commonly used teaching exercise in computer science involves a simple culinary task: making a sandwich. A teacher asks the students for instructions and follows them like a robot,

but if the instructions are not precise enough they can have unexpected results; for example, the instruction 'put the butter on the bread' can lead to the 'robot' picking up the entire tub of butter and putting it on top of the loaf of bread!

Another important question in mathematics is how complicated such algorithms can be to run. The computational complexity of a calculation is a measure of how many steps it takes. Adding or multiplying two numbers together is one calculation, but there are many more steps involved in tasks like finding a common factor or solving a system of equations. The performance of computers is measured in terms of how many calculations they can perform per second, and today's top Cray supercomputers run at over 10^{18} calculations per second.

We can also use computers to run machine-learning algorithms, which produce seemingly much more intelligent results – like being able to recognise images or classify and interpret large amounts of data. But they're still just using algorithms!

ALGORITHMS

A recipe, such as that for making pancakes, is a type of algorithm. It is a set of instructions for transforming the inputs – the raw ingredients – into an output – hopefully a tasty one! Algorithms can be described in different ways. A recipe is usually given as a list of ingredients followed by some numbered steps and perhaps a pretty picture of the finished dish. Other algorithms may be described using a flowchart. Instructions for computers are written using formal programming languages so that they are unambiguous.

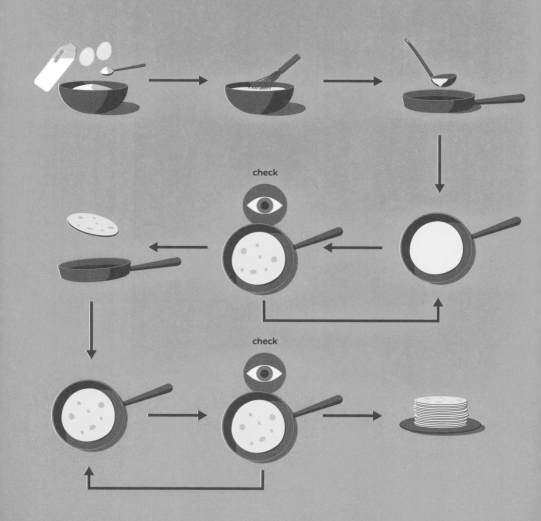

check

check

PROPOSITIONAL
LOGIC

SET
THEORY

PROOFS

VISUAL PROOFS

CHAPTER 3

LOGIC

BOOLEAN LOGIC

VENN DIAGRAMS

AXIOMS

CHAINS OF REASONING

INTRODUCTION

Logical thinking is a highly valuable skill – being able to work out the basic premises behind a situation and boil it down to simple logic, and then work out the best course of action, means you're well equipped to deal with everything the world has to throw at you. But as well as giving you the tools to simplify and solve real-world problems, logic can also be studied formally as a branch of mathematics – so you can prove that your solution to a problem is the best one.

The simplest form of logic is called **BOOLEAN LOGIC**, which reduces everything to a simple true or false value. Introduced by mathematician George Boole in the 1840s, it now underpins all of modern computing – by combining true or false values in different ways, creating a flow of logical values which can be used to perform complex computations, from simple addition to sophisticated artificial intelligence and machine learning.

PROPOSITIONAL LOGIC is the art of turning propositions – statements in words – into logical values, and considering how they interact when combined using conjunctions like *if* and *then.* If a shape has three sides, then it must be a triangle – but if a shape has four sides, that doesn't mean it's a square. We play a classic game of logic introduced by mathematician Charles Dodgson (better known as author Lewis Carroll), and see how simple reasoning can lead to mathematical breakthroughs.

An important concept in mathematics is that of **SET THEORY** – the study of collections of objects, and how they can be combined and compared. We can study sets of numbers – and as we saw in the previous chapter, such sets can be finite or infinite. We'll see how this relates to a famous mathematical paradox, and how sets underpin some of the basic rules of mathematical thought.

If you're interested in visualising sets, mathematician John Venn has the diagram for you. **VENN DIAGRAMS** are often used to represent interactions between different sets, easily displaying which collections an item belongs to. This has deep connections to ideas from both set theory and logic, and while they're often shared as fun memes, they're often useful in visualising important information and relationships.

One of the key goals of mathematics is to build a set of logical statements within a framework, in a way that allows others to use the facts we've discovered. Mathematicians use **PROOFS** to convince others of their ideas – if you see a mathematical pattern or relationship, you can formalise it using the language of proof, and once you know it's true you can share it as a fact with others.

The framework in which such proofs are completed starts from a set of basic principles: **AXIOMS** are mathematical statements which we take as our first assumptions – the foundations on which we can build all our other mathematical thinking. Mathematicians like Bertrand Russell worked hard to formalise the ideas of sets, axioms and logic so that future mathematicians could use them to construct more and more elaborate ideas.

While the examples used to illustrate logical ideas are often simple, the study of logic establishes the foundations of mathematics, and other mathematical ideas build on these basic principles to construct an elaborate tapestry of facts and truth we can use to understand the universe.

LOGIC MAP

SET THEORY
The study of sets: collections of elements which can be counted, combined and compared.

AXIOMS
Fixed starting points we can use as the basis of a deduction. Deciding on the axioms defines the system we're working in.

VENN DIAGRAMS
Developed by English logician John Venn, these diagrams allow us to present information about sets and their intersections using overlapping shapes.

EUCLID (FL. 300BCE)
Ancient Greek mathematician known as the 'father of geometry'. His *Elements* treatise outlined five axioms of geometry, along with many results that follow from them.

SETS

LOGIC
The science of making deductions based on truths and reasoning. Mathematically, it has many uses.

INCOMPLETENESS THEOREMS
Mathematical statements that it's impossible to prove either true or false, established by Austrian mathematician Kurt Gödel.

RUSSELL'S PARADOX

Popularised in 1901 by Bertrand Russell, based on earlier work by Zermelo, the paradox concerns the set of all sets that do not contain themselves. This set is a member of itself only if it is not a member of itself.

BOOLEAN LOGIC

Based on simple yes/no values, or 1s and 0s, Boolean logic is a form of algebra which lets us combine values using the operators AND, OR and NOT.

LOGIC GATES

In computer design, and theoretically, these manifest the Boolean operators as physical circuits.

OPERATORS

In computer programming, an operator is a type of function that is given one or more inputs and turns them into a single output.

PROOFS

Logical structures that mathematicians use to prove which of their ideas are always true.

IF ... THEN STATEMENTS

The key to propositional logic is statements like 'If A, then B'. If we know this, and also know A is true, we can infer B is true.

PROOFS

PYTHAGORAS' THEOREM

Theorem stating that the area of a square drawn on the hypotenuse (longest side) of a right-angled triangle is equal to the sum of the areas of squares drawn on the two shorter sides. There are hundreds of different proofs of the theorem, using algebraic, trigonometric and diagrammatic methods.

PROPOSITIONAL LOGIC

A branch of logic based on statements and inference. Statements like 'It's raining' and 'The washing is wet' can be linked using if ... then statements.

How does an idea from 1847 make computers work?

→ In 1847, George Boole developed a mathematical system to work with logical statements using just two values: true and false. Using the binary language of 1s and 0s together with logic gates, Boole's algebra underpins every electronic device we use today.

If you think about algebra, you probably imagine using letters to represent numbers, together with addition, subtraction, multiplication and division. Boolean algebra, introduced by George Boole in 1847, uses just two values: 'true' and 'false', often represented by 0 and 1, rather than the whole range of numbers, and instead of arithmetical operations it has logical operations: conjunction (AND), disjunction (OR) and negation (NOT).

A logic gate takes two inputs, each of which can be either 0 or 1, and turns it into an output. Each logic gate has its own symbol and processes the inputs in different ways. Imagine adding two numbers together. If our two inputs are 0 and 1, there are three possible answers: 0 (from 0 + 0), 1 (from 0 + 1 or 1 + 0), or 2 (from 1 + 1). By representing odd answers as 1 and even answers (0 or 2) as 0, we get a logic gate known as 'exclusive or', or XOR. Other logic gates include the AND gate, which outputs 1 only if both the inputs are 1, and the OR gate, which outputs 1 if either or both of the inputs are 1. The NOT gate takes a single input and inverts it, so if the input is 1 it outputs 0, and vice versa.

In the 20th century, electronics engineers began to build logic gates using switches. They used high and low voltages to represent 1s and 0s and designed circuits that took two inputs and gave the desired outputs for different types of logic gate. By chaining together logic gates, engineers built increasingly complex circuits. These chains of logic gates form the basis of computer processors and memory, without which our modern life would be very different indeed.

BINARY HALF-ADDER

A binary half-adder uses the logic gates XOR (exclusive or) and AND to add two binary digits, or bits, giving an output bit and a bit to say whether there is a 'carry' or not. The table shows the output and carry when we put 0 or 1 into the inputs A and B. Carrying digits may be familiar from base-10 arithmetic, when we add units to make a total bigger than 10. In binary arithmetic, we get a carry when we perform 1 + 1, because the number 2 is written 10 in binary.

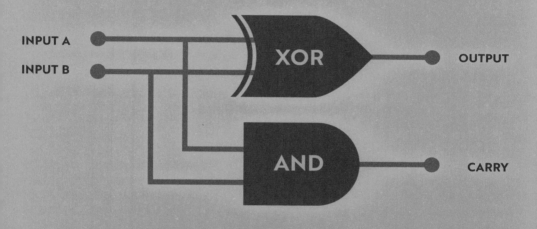

INPUT A	INPUT B	OUTPUT	CARRY
0	0	0	0
0	1	1	0
1	0	1	0
1	1	1	1

Can a baby manage a crocodile?

⟶ **According to a puzzle created by Lewis Carroll, babies are illogical, nobody who can manage a crocodile is despised, and illogical people are despised. Propositional logic allows us to deduce from these statements that babies cannot manage crocodiles.**

Lewis Carroll is best known for his book *Alice's Adventures in Wonderland*, but he was also a mathematician and wrote extensively about logic. The question of whether a baby can manage a crocodile appears in one of his works on propositional logic.

In propositional logic, we define relationships between statements, which are represented by letters, using connectives such as 'and', 'or', 'if ... then' and 'not'. Then we can make inferences, based on whether our statements are true or false, to construct logical arguments. The connectives serve the same purpose in propositional logic that logic gates serve in Boolean algebra.

Here are two statements that might be true or false: A: 'It is raining' and B: 'The path is wet'. We can link these statements with an 'if ... then' connective by saying 'If it is raining then the path is wet'. We can use an arrow to represent this, by writing A → B. Once we know this relationship exists between A and B, we can look at the path to see if it is wet. If it is not, we deduce that it can't be raining.

One common mistake that people make when manipulating logical statements is assuming that an if ... then statement works both ways. In the case of the wet path, we know that rain always leads to a wet path (A → B) but it's not necessarily the case that a wet path means it's raining. The path could be wet because it rained earlier or someone used a hosepipe.

The power of propositional logic is that from a set of established truths it is possible to deduce new truths. In mathematics, this deductive reasoning is at the heart of mathematical proof (see page 60). However, even if you're not planning to prove any mathematical theorems, familiarity with logical deduction is useful in many day-to-day scenarios, from figuring out why the washing isn't dry yet to winning family arguments about who should have fetched the washing in.

PROPOSITIONAL LOGIC

To answer the question 'Can a baby manage a crocodile?' we need to choose the right order in which to consider the three statements, or propositions, in Lewis Carroll's puzzle: (A) Babies are illogical; (B) Nobody who can manage a crocodile is despised; (C) Illogical people are despised. From the first proposition, we can deduce that if a person is a baby, they are not logical. Next, using the third proposition, that illogical persons are despised, we can deduce that babies are despised. Finally, knowing from the second proposition that nobody is despised who can manage a crocodile, our despised baby must therefore be unable to manage a crocodile.

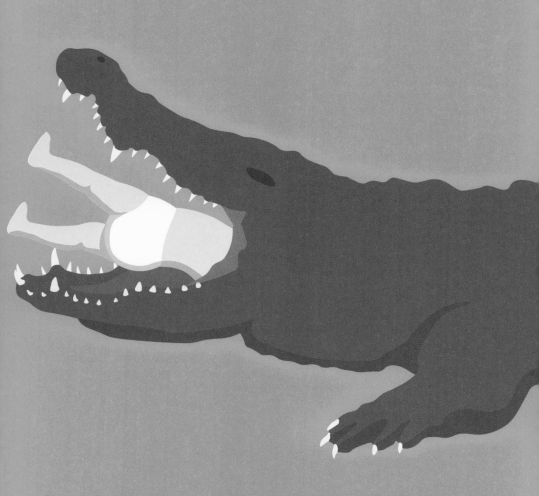

Who shaves the barber?

→ If a barber shaves only those who don't shave themselves, the barber cannot shave himself. This is an illustration of Russell's paradox, an important result in set theory.

Set theory is the branch of mathematics concerned with collections of objects. At a very early age, children learn how to categorise things and collect together toys that are alike in some way. The sets that mathematicians study are slightly more rigorously defined – and, unlike a child's set of toys, can be infinite as well as finite.

Mathematically speaking, a set is a collection of objects: numbers, points, lines or shapes. Each object in the collection is called an element, or member, of the set. Sets are often denoted using curly brackets, so we could write {1, 2, 3} to represent the set of numbers from one to three. The order doesn't matter, so the set {1, 3, 2} is equivalent to the set {1, 2, 3}. The number of elements in a set is called its cardinality. There is a set that has no elements, called the empty set, whose cardinality is zero.

Set theory has its origins in the work of Georg Cantor in the late 19th century. One of Cantor's most important discoveries was his proof that some sets, including the set of all real numbers, are uncountable (see page 24 for more about different sizes of infinity). Early set theory was defined informally, using natural language, but this meant that contradictions or paradoxes could be formed. Russell's paradox is one such example, concerning the set of all sets that are not members of themselves. The paradox was discovered independently by Ernst Zermelo in 1899 and Bertrand Russell in 1901 and has been illustrated in many ways, including the barber paradox.

Realising that the informal definitions of naive set theory led to paradoxes, Zermelo developed an axiomatic framework for set theory. An axiomatic framework is a rigorous set of starting points or axioms together with the rules that can be used to develop theorems from those axioms. Together with additions by Abraham Fraenkel, this became known as Zermelo–Fraenkel set theory and is the most commonly used foundation for modern mathematics.

RUSSELL'S PARADOX

The barber shaves all, and only, people who don't shave themselves. If the barber doesn't shave himself, then he must shave himself, since he shaves everyone who doesn't shave themselves. But he can't both shave himself and not shave himself. This is an example of Russell's paradox. The paradox can be resolved by imagining a barber who doesn't need to shave at all (perhaps they are naturally free from facial hair) – but the underlying problem of self-referential sets needs to be considered when developing a set-theoretic approach to mathematics.

What type of person was John Venn?

→ If we drew a Venn diagram to represent different types of people, John Venn, who popularised the Venn diagram, would be in the overlap between the sets of mathematicians, Anglican priests and people with bushy beards.

A Venn diagram shows logical relationships between sets visually. Imagine we have two sets: A, the set of mammals; and B, the set of things that can fly. Create two overlapping circles labelled A and B, dividing the page into four regions. A cat goes in circle A, because cats are mammals but can't fly. A swan goes in circle B, because swans can fly but aren't mammals. A bat goes in the overlap, because it's a mammal that can fly. Finally, frogs, which aren't mammals and can't fly, go in the fourth region, outside both circles.

Venn diagrams are useful for explaining elementary set theory. They are also a visually appealing way to represent relationships between ideas and have become popular as an internet meme format. Venn diagrams are often mistaken for another diagrammatic way of showing relationships between sets – the Euler diagram. Like Venn diagrams, Euler diagrams use overlapping circles to show hierarchies and relationships, but unlike Venn diagrams, they don't necessarily show every possible relationship, only the relevant ones.

Since Venn diagrams have to show every possible relationship, a Venn diagram for two sets has four regions and a Venn diagram for three sets has eight regions. This generalises to 2^n regions for n sets – for every new set we add, the shape representing that set has to intersect with all the regions that are already there, which doubles the number of regions.

Although he was not the first person to represent data using overlapping regions, John Venn found a general way to construct diagrams for any number of sets, by adding curves that intersect with all the previous ones, and so diagrams of this type now bear his name.

VENN DIAGRAMS

This Venn diagram shows some of the sets that John Venn belonged to – he was a mathematician and an Anglican priest with a beard. To decide where you would belong, answer the following questions. Are you a mathematician? Do you have a beard? Are you an Anglican priest? Once you have your answers, you should be able to figure out which section of the diagram describes the set to which you belong.

HAS A BEARD

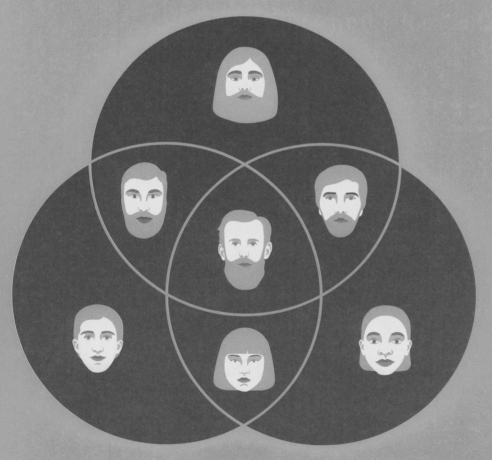

IS A MATHEMATICIAN   **IS AN ANGLICAN PRIEST**

How can you turn an idea into a fact?

⟶ **Mathematical conjectures are ideas which mathematicians have reason to believe are true but have not yet been proved. Finding a rigorous logical proof changes the status from conjecture to theorem – from idea to fact.**

The concept of proving things mathematically can be traced back to ancient Greek geometry. Philosophers were interested in how to establish whether ideas were true or not, and geometry offered a way to construct logical deductions from starting points that everyone could agree on. (These starting points are known as *axioms*; see page 62.) The general concept of a mathematical proof is that if everyone can agree on the starting points and each deduction from those starting points has no logical flaws, then we reach an end point which is proven to be true.

As mathematical thinking and techniques developed through medieval times, Islamic scholars introduced arithmetical and algebraic ways of proving mathematical statements which did not rely on geometric intuition. Over time, mathematicians refined these methods, and by using previously proven results as building blocks for new proofs, the landscape of proven mathematical knowledge expanded.

Modern mathematicians write proofs using rigorous notation that can be unambiguously interpreted by their colleagues, and before a result is accepted by the mathematical community as fact, the proof has to be checked. When Andrew Wiles presented his proof of Fermat's last theorem in 1993, mathematicians were very excited because people had been trying to prove it for hundreds of years. In the process of checking the proof, a flaw was discovered, and it took another year for Wiles to finally complete his proof.

Computers are now an integral part of mathematical proof as they can be used to check cases or perform calculations that would take too long for humans to do by hand. The first major theorem to be proved with the help of computers was the four-colour theorem in the 1970s. This theorem states that any map can be coloured with at most four colours so that no two regions which touch are the same colour.

VISUAL PROOFS

Visual proofs, or proofs without words, are not proofs in a formal mathematical sense because they do not include a logical argument. However, they provide valuable insight into mathematical results, and can give a useful starting point for constructing a rigorous proof. These diagrams form a visual proof that the square on the hypotenuse of a right-angled triangle is equal to the sum of the squares on the two shorter sides – you may recognise this as Pythagoras' theorem.

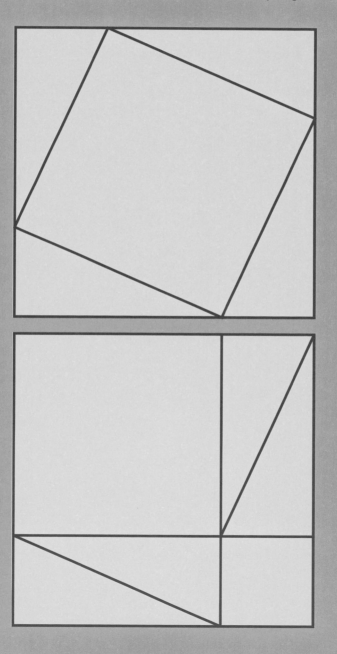

How many pages does it take to prove 1 + 1 = 2?

⟶ To prove that 1 + 1 = 2, we need to know what our starting points, or axioms, are. Mathematicians Whitehead and Russell famously took several hundred pages to establish the axioms, notation and rigorous logical steps needed for this proof.

The equation 1 + 1 = 2 seems so straightforward that it's hard to imagine why it would need proving – but mathematicians don't like to assume that something is true just because it seems obvious. To prove it, we need to know what we can assume as our starting points, also called axioms or postulates.

In their 1910 work *Principia Mathematica*, Whitehead and Russell attempted to provide a consistent foundation for mathematics, free from paradoxes. They defined numbers in terms of sets: the number 1 is the set of all sets containing exactly one element. They then described a formal and rigorous definition of addition. The proof that 1 + 1 = 2 took hundreds of pages because Russell and Whitehead aimed to define exactly what is meant by '1', '+', '=' and '2'. Once they proved the result, they made the delightfully understated comment 'The above proposition is occasionally useful'.

Until the 19th century, the foundation of mathematical thinking was based on the postulates in Euclid's *Elements*, an ancient Greek treatise on geometry from around 300 BCE. As mathematics became more abstract, mathematicians became concerned that geometry was no longer sufficient to rigorously underpin all mathematical thought. This was the motivation for developing frameworks based on set theory, and for a while it was believed that it would be possible to come up with a complete set of axioms on which all mathematics could be built.

In the 1930s, Kurt Gödel announced his incompleteness theorems, which demonstrated that no matter what axioms are chosen as the foundations of arithmetic, there will always be some statements which can be neither proved nor disproved. This makes it difficult to conceive of a single unified set of axioms that serve as the foundation for all mathematical thought, but within individual branches of mathematics, mathematicians are very happy to continue researching and proving ideas from accepted sets of axioms for each discipline.

CHAINS OF REASONING

A mathematical proof is a chain of logical deductions rather like a domino run. Each step in the proof depends on the steps before it being correct, and if any step is missing, or flawed, the proof cannot run through to its conclusion. However, every domino run has to start with a first domino being pushed over, and these first steps are our axioms – the foundations on which the rest of our mathematical thinking is built.

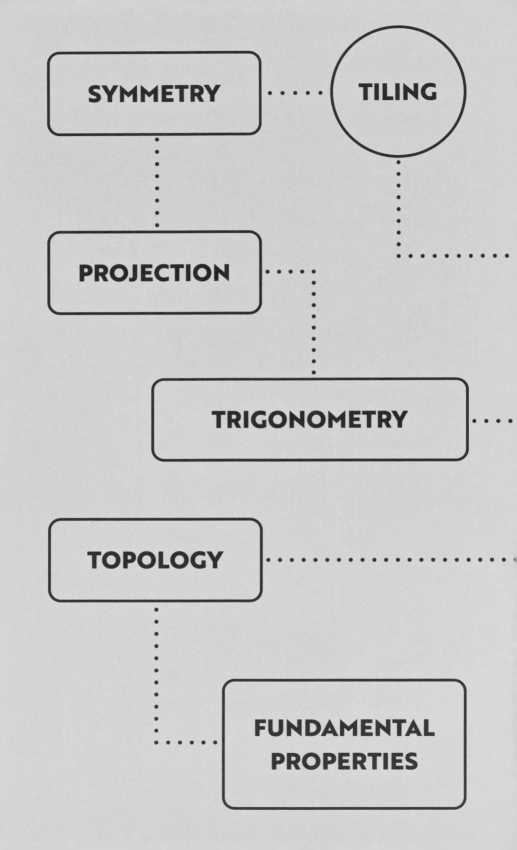

CHAPTER 4

GEOMETRY AND SHAPE

SHAPES

CURVATURE

INTRODUCTION

From a very early age, we're taught two fundamental concepts from mathematics: numbers and **SHAPES**. Every small child learns the difference between a **CIRCLE** and a square, and the idea and study of shape forms a huge part of mathematics at a much higher level too.

GEOMETRY – from the Greek words for 'the earth' and 'measurement' – was originally concerned with measuring areas of land. It was hugely important for agricultural societies, who needed to understand the relationship between the shape and measurements of a piece of land and its area, which would dictate how many crops it could produce.

As time has gone on, geometry has found useful applications in many more areas – engineering, architecture and art have all benefited from a better understanding of shapes and their measurements. Mathematicians have many ways to describe and categorise shapes, including **SYMMETRY**. Neat, symmetrical shapes like squares and hexagons have very useful properties, and understanding the patterns present in the shape of an object or design can help us to make sense of it.

Two-dimensional shapes like hexagons and squares fall into the category of polygons, and three-dimensional shapes like cubes and pyramids are called polyhedra. Thinking about shapes in three dimensions adds, quite literally, a whole new dimension – and as we'll see, some surprises can be hiding in even a simple shape like a cube.

Another place symmetry can be found is in **TILINGS** or tessellations – two-dimensional patterns made from simple polygons and other shapes, which can repeat in a regular pattern, or, in some cases, go on forever without repeating. In practical terms, we can use tilings to decorate surfaces, but studying the different ways shapes fit together gives us insights into shapes and symmetry. New **REGULAR TILINGS** are being discovered even now, with a new way to cover the plane with pentagons found as recently as 2015.

Those who have studied geometry may be familiar with **TRIGONOMETRY**, from the ancient Greek for 'triangle' and 'measure'. The idea of measuring triangles, which links to various other mathematical ideas like π (pi), has many uses throughout engineering, physics and geometry. We'll see how it can be used to find accurate values for heights – even if they're too high to climb up and measure yourself!

As well as rigid polyhedra like cubes, geometry also involves smooth round shapes like spheres and cylinders. **CURVATURE** dictates the way a round shape will behave – even creating a whole new type of geometry on its surface.

And speaking of curved surfaces, we couldn't leave out **TOPOLOGY** – this is the mathematical study of the fundamental properties of shapes, in any number of dimensions. Since these properties are independent of the size, and often the specific shape, of an object, topologists consider shapes to be the same if they can be smoothly deformed into each other, without tearing or sticking together – which explains why some mathematicians can't tell their doughnut from their cup of coffee!

GEOMETRY AND SHAPES MAP

SHAPES

FUNDAMENTAL PROPERTIES

Properties which are key to the structure of a topological object, and not unique to the specific shape. For example, we could consider a doughnut to be the same as a mug with a handle if we focus on only the number of holes.

REGULAR TILING

A tiling in which all shapes are the same. The only regular shapes that can tile a plane without leaving gaps are squares, triangles and hexagons.

TOPOLOGY

Concerns the fundamental shape of an object, regardless of if you stretch, squash or deform it. Sometimes called rubber sheet geometry.

TILING

The arrangement of shapes on a two-dimensional plane with no gaps or overlaps. Also called tessellation.

SHAPES

Figures composed of straight lines and/or curves. There are many familiar geometric shapes, including simple polygons and 3D polyhedra. We can categorise shapes by their sides or faces, and also study irregular shapes and those with no straight edges at all.

SYMMETRY

A shape has symmetry if you can change it in some way, e.g. by reflecting or rotating it, without changing the way it looks.

CIRCLE

A shape defined as all the points an equal distance from a central point. A circle can be rotated by any angle, or reflected in any direction, and it will look exactly the same – it has infinitely many symmetries.

POLYGON

A two-dimensional shape whose sides are all straight lines.

GEOMETRY

PROJECTION
The shadow of a shape from a particular direction. We can study shapes by considering their projections from different directions. Projections can reveal hidden structure in familiar objects.

GEOMETRY
The branch of mathematics dealing with points, lines, angles, surfaces and solids. Geometry allows us to understand shapes, but it can also be applied to more abstract ideas like higher-dimensional objects.

CURVATURE
A geometrical property defining how a shape curves in space, and how geometry behaves on the shape's surface.

TRIGONOMETRY
The study of triangles and the relationships between their angles and sides.

SPHERICAL GEOMETRY
The study of the properties of objects on the surface of a sphere, where parallel straight lines always cross twice and the angles in a triangle add up to more than 180 degrees.

POLYHEDRON
A three-dimensional shape whose faces are all polygons.

What is the most symmetrical shape?

⟶ Most people have an intuitive idea of what symmetry means, but mathematicians use symmetry groups to precisely define the symmetries of a shape. The circle is the most symmetrical shape because it has the largest symmetry group.

A symmetry is an action you can perform on a shape that leaves it looking the same as when you started. For example, you could turn a blank sheet of paper 180° and nobody would know that you had moved it. A symmetry group is a group (see page 34) that contains all the symmetries of a shape.

For example, think about the actions you could perform on a square. You could do nothing – which counts as an action, called the identity. This would leave all four corners in their original positions. You could rotate it around the centre by 90°, 180° or 270°; after any of these moves the square would look the same, but if you labelled the corners you would see that they had different positions after each rotation.

You could also reflect the square (either in a line through the midpoints of two opposite sides, or in a line through two opposite corners) and then rotate it by 0°, 90°, 180°

or 270°. This gives four new positions for the corners, making a total of eight symmetries. Any other combination of reflections and rotations would give one of the eight positions already seen.

For regular two-dimensional shapes (those with all sides the same length and all angles the same size), the number of symmetries goes up as the number of sides goes up. A regular pentagon has 10 symmetries and a regular hexagon has 12. The logical conclusion of this process leads to a circle. You can rotate a circle by any amount you like and it will look the same, so it has an infinite number of symmetries. What's more, you can reflect it first and then rotate it, thereby doubling the number of symmetries (although double infinity is still infinity – see page 24). So the symmetry group of a circle is infinite, making the circle the most symmetrical two-dimensional shape.

SYMMETRIES OF A CUBE

To find the symmetries of a cube, count lines that pass through the centre. There are three through the midpoints of opposite faces, around which you can rotate the cube 90°, 180° or 270°. There are four through diagonally opposite corners, around which you can rotate the cube 120° or 240°. There are six through the midpoints of diagonally opposite edges, around which you can rotate the cube 180°. Adding the identity gives 24 symmetries. Then you can reflect before carrying out any of those rotations, for a total of 48 symmetries.

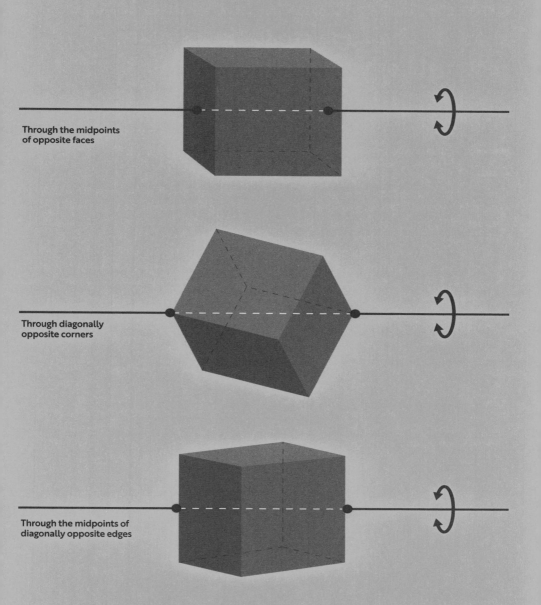

Through the midpoints of opposite faces

Through diagonally opposite corners

Through the midpoints of diagonally opposite edges

What shape is a cube's shadow?

→ The geometry of shadows is a fascinating subject that can lead to some unexpected outcomes. For example, the shadow of a cube could be a square, a rectangle or even a hexagon.

A square is a two-dimensional shape with four equal sides and four right angles, and a cube is a three-dimensional shape with six square faces. So how can a cube have a hexagonal shadow? It all depends on its position. If you hold a cube over a table and shine a light from directly overhead, the shadow it casts will be square. But if you let one edge touch the table and tilt the cube by 45°, the shadow becomes a rectangle.

You can find the shape of an object's shadow by taking slices through the object, perpendicular to the direction the light is coming from. The highest point of the tilted cube is now a straight edge. If you were to take slices moving downwards, the first few would cut a thin piece off one edge of the cube and the chunks would get wider as you move down. The widest slice would be at the middle, when you're cutting all the way across the cube between two diagonally opposite edges; this is the part that casts the shadow.

To find a hexagonal shadow you can tilt the cube in a different way, so that only one corner is touching the table, with the diagonally opposite corner directly above. Now the highest point is this diagonally opposite corner. If you repeat the slice-taking process, the first few slices will take triangular wedges, getting bigger as you go down. Slices near the centre will make hexagons, and again, the widest slice will be through the middle, cutting through the midpoint of the edges of the cube; this central hexagon casts the shadow.

These ideas can be hard to visualise, and mathematicians often use physical props to help their thought processes. A torch and a dice, or a Rubik's cube if you happen to have one, can make the concepts startlingly clear!

SURPRISING SHADOWS

Just as mathematicians explore three-dimensional objects through their shadows, so shadow artists make use of different light angles to weave and animate intriguing tales. Even hand shadows, one of the most basic forms of shadow art, can throw up some surprises. With careful arrangement, it's possible to make two or three different animals from the same hand position, depending on the angle the light is coming from.

What shapes can you use to tile your bathroom?

⟶ In a tile shop you'll be unlikely to see anything other than squares and rectangles. But technically it would be possible to use many other shapes, including curved ones.

In mathematics this is known as tiling the 2D plane: fitting together (or tessellating) shapes so that they cover a flat surface without leaving any gaps. Squares and rectangles make good tiles because they have four right angles, and 4 × 90° = 360°. This makes a full turn, so wherever four corners meet, they line up neatly with no gaps. Six equilateral triangles, with angles of 60°, or three regular hexagons, with angles of 120°, also work. In fact, any quadrilateral (four-sided shape) will tessellate, as will any triangle. It's also possible to create tilings that use more than one shape. For example, a combination of regular octagons and squares will tile the plane, as will a combination of regular hexagons, equilateral triangles and squares.

It's not possible to tile with regular pentagons – they have angles of 108°, so three meeting at a point would leave a gap of 36°, but four would overlap. However, there are 15 types of irregular pentagon that will tile the

plane. You can make an example of such a pentagon by dividing a regular hexagon into three identical pieces: draw lines from the midpoints of three non-touching sides to the centre to make pentagons with three 120° angles and two right angles.

Circles cannot tile the plane. But you can create a tessellating shape from a circle by cutting two quarter-circle holes out of it. This leaves a shape called a scallop that looks a bit like a fancy umbrella; the top part is a semicircle and bottom part is a curved point that fits between two circles. Putting two of them next to each other leaves spaces where the same shape can fit, and this can be continued indefinitely, giving a pattern that looks like fish scales.

The Dutch artist M. C. Escher (1898–1972) used mathematical ideas in many of his works. He created surprising tilings made of animals that, at first glance, look as though they shouldn't tessellate – making it all the more satisfying when you realise that they do.

TILINGS AND TESSELLATIONS

With a little imagination you can create many shapes that will tessellate, so long as any parts that stick out have a matching space to fit into. Many beautiful and complex examples of both straight-edged and curved tiles can be seen in Islamic architecture. But note that the skill and time taken to create these is incredible – something to bear in mind when you're deciding how to redecorate your bathroom!

How can you measure a tree without climbing it?

⟶ **You'll need three things: a tape measure, a clinometer (which is a device for measuring angles) and a basic knowledge of trigonometry. With a couple of measurements you can calculate the height.**

Trigonometry is the study of triangles, in particular of how their angles and the lengths of their sides are related. The main trigonometric tools are sine, cosine and tangent, and in a right-angled triangle you can apply these to one of the angles to find the ratio of two sides. The one you'll need for your tree measurement is the tangent, which is the ratio of the side that isn't touching the angle (called the opposite) to the shorter of the sides that is touching it (called the adjacent).

The angle you need to measure is the one between the ground where you're standing and a straight line to the top of the tree. The two sides of the triangle are the height of the tree (the opposite) and the distance from the base of the tree to the point where you're standing (the adjacent). These two

lengths make a right angle, which means you can use the tangent of the angle you measured to relate them. (If the tree is on a hill then it might not make a right angle with the ground, which makes things a bit more complicated, but it can still be done.) The third side of the triangle, which you don't need for the calculation, is the distance from the top of the tree to the point where you're standing – this is the longest side in the triangle, called the hypotenuse.

You can measure the angle with a clinometer, and you can measure the adjacent side of the triangle with a tape measure along the ground. Once you have your measurements, you can use them in the formula: height of tree = distance along ground × tangent of angle. That's significantly quicker and safer than climbing to the top of the tree!

ENVIRONMENTAL RESEARCH

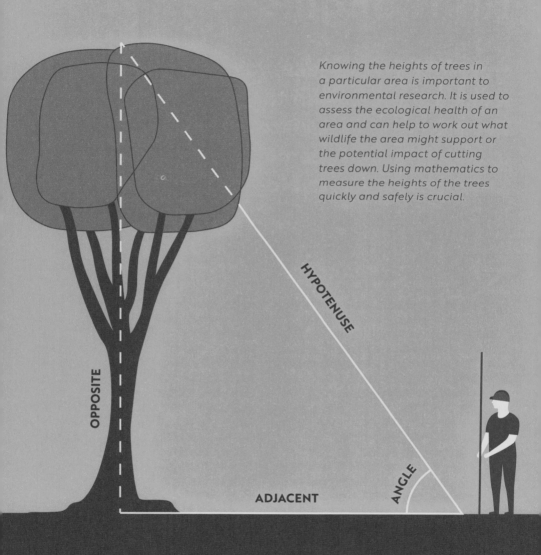

Knowing the heights of trees in a particular area is important to environmental research. It is used to assess the ecological health of an area and can help to work out what wildlife the area might support or the potential impact of cutting trees down. Using mathematics to measure the heights of the trees quickly and safely is crucial.

HYPOTENUSE

OPPOSITE

ANGLE

ADJACENT

How can you make a triangle with three right angles?

⟶ **On a flat surface, you can't make a triangle with three right angles. But on a curved surface like the surface of a sphere, this seemingly impossible task becomes possible.**

The standard geometry that most people are familiar with, where the three angles in a triangle add up to 180°, is called Euclidean geometry after the ancient Greek mathematician Euclid. His treatise *Elements* contains proofs of hundreds of geometrical theorems and is still used as a reference book today. But all the theorems in the *Elements* apply to geometry on a flat surface (called a plane). For geometry on a curved surface, different rules apply.

There are two main types of non-Euclidean geometry: elliptical and hyperbolic. Elliptical geometry takes place on a surface with positive curvature. This means that the surface always curves away from a given point in the same way. For example, from the top of a sphere the surface curves downwards no matter what direction you look in.

Hyperbolic geometry takes place on a surface with negative curvature. This means that the surface curves away from a point in different ways, depending on the direction.

This is slightly harder to visualise, but you can think of a curvy potato chip or a saddle, which curve upwards along one axis and downwards along the other.

On both an elliptical and a hyperbolic surface, straight lines become curves. Despite this, many rules of Euclidean geometry still apply. The key difference can be seen by looking at parallel lines (lines that never meet). In Euclidean geometry, for a given line and a point that isn't on the line, there is exactly one line through the point that is parallel to the original line. Any other line through that point will intersect the original line somewhere.

In elliptical geometry, lines curve towards one another. This means any two lines will intersect at some point, so parallel lines do not exist in this geometry. In hyperbolic geometry, lines curve away from one another. So in this case, for any given line and a point that isn't on the line, there are infinitely many lines parallel to the original line.

NON-EUCLIDEAN TRIANGLES

In Euclidean geometry, the angles in a triangle always sum to 180°. In elliptical geometry, the curvature means that the sum is always greater than 180°, and this allows us to draw a triangle with three right angles. A polar bear starting from the north pole could walk south, then east, then north and end up back where it started. In hyperbolic geometry, the sum is always less than 180° – a polar bear trying to do the same thing on this surface would end up very lost!

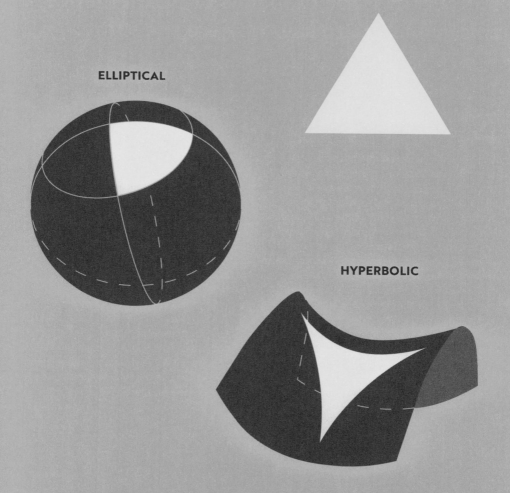

EUCLIDEAN

ELLIPTICAL

HYPERBOLIC

Is a mountain the same as a molehill?

→ Common sense tells us that a mountain is not the same as a molehill. But – putting aside details of scale – they are both essentially just bumps in an otherwise flat surface. In some branches of mathematics, this is enough to say they are the same.

Topology is a branch of mathematics in which objects are considered to be 'the same' if one of them could morph into the other by stretching, twisting or otherwise deforming. The only manipulations that are not allowed are making or closing up a hole. Forget the physical properties of the material an object is made from – the question is: if you could stretch, squash and bend an object as much as you like, could you make it the same shape as some other object?

For example, what about a slice of bread and a bedsheet? These are both flat, rectangular objects so, if the bread were made of extremely stretchy dough, you could easily squash it to make it as thin as a bedsheet and then stretch it out to the same dimensions. So, to topologists, a slice of bread is the same as a bedsheet. Now, what about

a slice of bread and a beaker? This is not so immediately obvious, but you could lift the edges of the bread to create sides and squash out any bumps to make a beaker shape. So a slice of bread, a bedsheet and a beaker are all topologically the same.

Now, what about a pair of trousers? Here we hit a problem. You could stretch the bread out to resemble a piece of fabric large enough to make a pair of trousers, but there's no way to make that piece of fabric into a pair of trousers without sticking edges together or cutting holes. So a pair of trousers is topologically different.

It might seem like a strange idea, but this process of focusing on what is the same about two objects or situations, and ignoring what is different, allows mathematicians to use tools from one area of mathematics to solve problems in a completely different area.

ABSTRACTION

Abstraction, a key skill in mathematics, means finding the underlying structure or pattern in a concept regardless of its properties in real life. In the physical world, it's important to know that a mountain is a huge rocky structure whereas a molehill is a small pile of earth.

In the mathematical world, the use of abstraction allows us to consider only the properties that are important to the question at hand while disregarding irrelevant factors. This helps us to find useful solutions without overcomplicating the calculations.

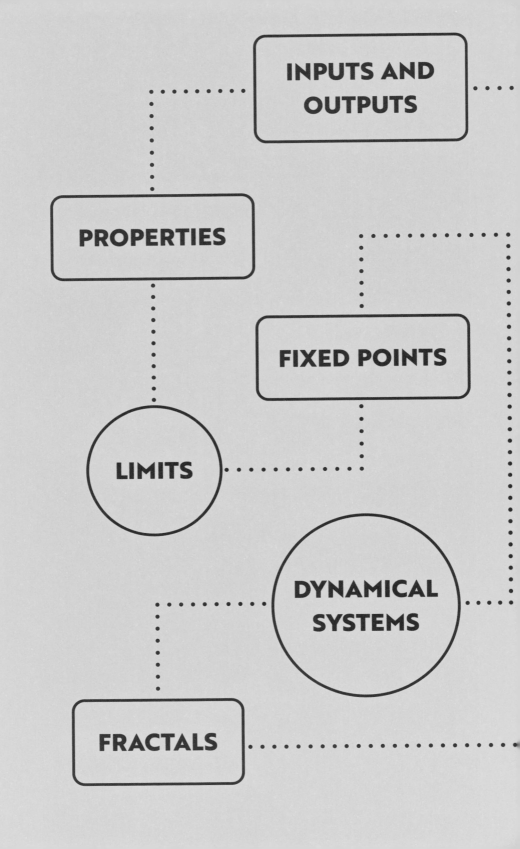

CHAPTER 5

FUNCTIONS

RIEMANN HYPOTHESIS

CHAOS

INTRODUCTION

Without realising it, we all use functions every day. A function is a rule for deciding what to do in a given situation: simply, given an input, what output should result? Whether it's deciding which bin to place a piece of recycling into or calculating the amount of change to give someone in a shop, every decision or processing task can be thought of as a function, or map.

MATHEMATICAL FUNCTIONS can be much more precisely defined. As well as describing what output we'd expect for a given input, we can define the set of possible valid inputs to the function, and the range of possible outputs we might expect. We also have certain rules we expect the function to follow in order to make sure it's possible to apply it, and conditions that determine whether the function can be undone or inverted.

The area of maths dedicated to studying functions is called **ANALYSIS**, and it allows us to pick apart the fine details – how exactly do we define when a function's graph is smooth, and what does it mean if you enter extremely similar inputs but get a very different output?

The notion of a 'well-behaved' function takes this one step further – the types of functions mathematicians like to work with are ones which behave in sensible, predictable ways, and we understand how these functions work more deeply than those that are less well defined. **CONTINUOUS FUNCTIONS** are an important notion, and we'll also see how some functions can get closer and closer to a particular value without ever reaching it.

The study of functions is a large part of **DYNAMICAL SYSTEMS** – the study of the behaviour of processes over time. The movement of planets, the motion of liquids and gases, and even fluctuations in the stock market can all be modelled using simple functions, but when those functions are applied thousands of times a second you need to use dynamics to understand the long-term behaviour.

A lovely outcome from studying dynamics is the incredible visualisations that result from studying the long-term behaviour of functions – **FRACTALS** are infinitely detailed images that can encapsulate the behaviour of dynamical systems when you allow things to run forever. Much like the systems they model, fractals can be described using very simple rules, which when repeated over and over generate complex, beautiful structures.

Another related concept is that of mathematical **CHAOS** – a system might be defined in terms of simple functions, but that doesn't mean it's easy to predict how the behaviour of the system will change if you change the input values. The so-called 'butterfly effect' means that a tiny change in the input can result in a vastly different output, and mathematicians understand only too well how difficult it can be to model systems like weather patterns; while the individual motions of air particles and temperature changes can be simply modelled, the whole system iterated over time becomes inherently chaotic.

We couldn't finish a chapter on functions without mentioning one of the most famous – the Zeta function, responsible for one of mathematics' greatest unsolved puzzles, the **RIEMANN HYPOTHESIS**. The Zeta function takes inputs from the complex plane and spits out complex numbers – but it's the source of a deep, long-standing mystery, which connects to prime numbers and a variety of other mathematical ideas.

FUNCTIONS MAP

MATHEMATICAL FUNCTIONS

Mathematical operations which take in one or more values as an input and return a result as an output. They come in many types, and are used in many areas of mathematics.

FUNCTIONS

ANALYSIS

The area of mathematics dedicated to studying functions.

SUMS OF SERIES

Adding together a series of numbers can be thought of as a function. As the number of terms in the series increases to infinity, sometimes they can behave in unexpected ways.

LIMIT

A value that the output of a function approaches as the input approaches a particular value, such as zero or infinity. Limits let us study extreme behaviour and understand functions better.

RIEMANN ZETA FUNCTION

A mathematical function that connects the study of numbers and functions with the distribution of prime numbers.

CONTINUOUS FUNCTIONS

Functions in which changing the input very slightly changes the output by only a small amount. This means they have no unexpected jumps or undefined points.

RIEMANN HYPOTHESIS

Unsolved problem concerning which input values to the Riemann zeta function give an output of zero. We think we know what all of them are, but nobody's managed to prove it yet. Solving the Riemann Hypothesis might help us to understand the apparent patterns in prime numbers.

INVERTIBLE FUNCTIONS

Functions which have a unique mapping of inputs to outputs, so that the function can be inverted and outputs mapped back to their inputs.

LOGISTIC MAP

A function used to model population growth. The behaviour of the model is simple for small parameter values, but it quickly becomes chaotic.

CHAOS

A system is called chaotic if a small change in the input to a dynamical system results in a large unpredictable change to the end results.

FIXED POINTS

Values in a dynamical system for which the output from the function is the same as the value you put in. Can be *repelling*, meaning successive values will diverge away from the point, or *attracting*, meaning points nearby will follow paths which converge to the point.

DETERMINISTIC

Dynamical systems are deterministic, meaning there is no randomness involved and future states can always be fully determined from the current one.

ITERATION

SIERPIŃSKI TRIANGLE

A fractal, named after Polish mathematician Wacław Sierpiński, that is usually made by repeatedly removing the centre of an equilateral triangle. The same structure can be created in a variety of other ways by repeated application of different functions.

DYNAMICAL SYSTEMS

The result of applying a function repeatedly to see how the result behaves long-term. Can be used to model real-world systems.

FRACTALS

Beautiful, complex visualisations which often result from plotting the behaviour of dynamical systems.

Why can't you un-square a number?

⟶ Squaring a number is a mathematical operation everyone learns in school – to square a number, you multiply it by itself. The opposite of this is called taking the square root, but this can lead to more than one answer...

Most mathematical ideas or structures involve taking an object and manipulating it in some way to get a result. The idea of a function allows us to formalise this, and we can think of a function as a notional machine that takes in an input and spits out an output.

When defining a function, we consider the range of possible inputs, which is often just numbers, but could also be a smaller set like integers (see page 18), or a different type of object, shapes, vectors (see page 38) or even functions themselves. The range of possible outputs from the function might be the same as the inputs – or, depending on the function, it could be completely different. The function which takes in a number x and returns a tree with the number x carved into it is a perfectly valid function!

Another important property of a function is how it maps the inputs to the outputs. It could be that every input has a unique output – or many inputs could map to the same output. For a function to be well defined, we need each distinct input to give us a uniquely defined output, otherwise we can't say what the result of applying the function will be.

In the case of the squaring function, this is true – given a number x, the result x^2 is uniquely defined. But going the other way is more complicated, and in this case some inputs give the same output as others – for example, the square of 2 is 4, but the square of −2 is also 4. This means the function isn't 'one-to-one', so it can't be undone without some extra information. If you asked a mathematician to tell you the square root of 4, they'd probably say it's 'plus or minus 2'.

FUNCTIONS

Functions are used to map inputs to outputs in different ways. Depending on the function, you might have each input giving a unique output (a one-to-one function, sometimes called injective). It may be that all possible values of the output are mapped to by some input, in which case we say the function is 'onto', or surjective. If both are true, it's called a bijective function, and the function can be inverted and used to map the other way. Some functions, called constant functions, map every input to a single value.

BIJECTIVE
(injective and surjective)

x + 1

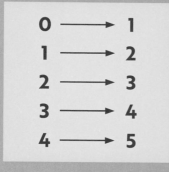

Whole numbers → Whole numbers

INJECTIVE
(but not surjective)

x (maps any input to itself)

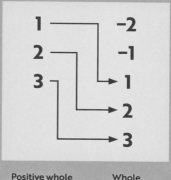

Positive whole numbers → Whole numbers

SURJECTIVE
(but not injective)

Nearest whole number

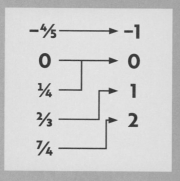

Fractions → Whole numbers

CONSTANT
(neither injective nor surjective)

2, whatever the input

Whole numbers → Whole numbers

What does it mean for a function to be 'well-behaved'?

→ Functions that behave in predictable ways – generating a single output for every input without any sudden jumps – are called 'well-behaved' because they are easier to use, and more helpful, than other functions.

We often use the term 'well-behaved' to describe a function (see page 88) which satisfies a few useful conditions.

First, the function must be defined everywhere – for all the inputs you could give, there's a way to determine the answer. The function 'write down the third digit of a number' only works for numbers with three or more digits – you need to define the set of inputs you're using carefully.

Second, the function must give a single value. Some functions can't be inverted because doing so would lead to a function for which one input could give more than one output – for example, the square root function on numbers, for which 4 can give both −2 and 2. Such a function can't be sensibly studied, because there needs to be a well-defined output for every possible input.

We also want functions to be continuous – a specific mathematical term which means that if you change the input to a function very slightly, it'll only change the output slightly.

For example, the doubling function would take 2 to 4, but if we start at 2.00001, we'd get 4.00002, which is still very close to 4 – and this function is continuous.

Functions that aren't continuous are usually characterised by unexpected sudden jumps when drawn on a graph – for example, the delta function, which takes a value of 0 for negative numbers and 1 for positive numbers, isn't continuous, as it has a step at the point 0. Most simple functions that can be plotted on a graph with a single straight or curved line are continuous.

Another nice property of a function is having a derivative. This means we can use calculus, the study of rates of change, to model real-world processes (see page 134). Roughly, the derivative corresponds to the steepness of the line when you plot the function on a graph, which means some functions (including non-continuous ones with strange jumps or gaps) don't have a well-defined derivative, as the slope of the line isn't defined at the discontinuity.

CONTINUOUS FUNCTIONS

*Continuous functions give
mathematicians a smoother ride
– we understand them better and
can predict how they'll behave and
interact with each other. Sometimes
we do have to work with other types
of function, but there are techniques
we can use – such as looking at
only the part of the function where
it is continuous, or smoothing over
discontinuities – to allow us to apply
existing tools to study them.*

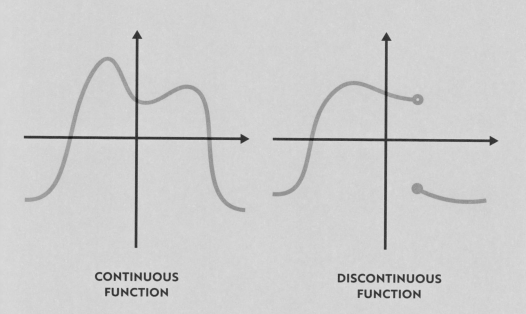

**CONTINUOUS
FUNCTION**

**DISCONTINUOUS
FUNCTION**

How can you drink infinitely many beers without getting drunk?

→ It depends on your definition of 'a beer'. It's possible to construct an infinite sequence of numbers, always getting smaller, which add up to a finite total – if your beers get smaller fast enough, you can stay under the limit!

A classic maths joke involves infinitely many mathematicians walking into a pub – the first orders a pint of beer, the second half a pint, the third orders a quarter of a pint... The bartender isn't amused, and the punchline to the joke hinges on what would happen next.

If we continue this sequence logically, each mathematician ordering half the amount of the previous, the sequence could continue forever, with smaller drinks each time. We can find the total amount of beer by pouring them all into the same glass (ignoring the initial pint, which we can leave the first mathematician to drink in peace).

Half a pint of beer would half-fill a second glass. Adding a further quarter-pint would take up half the remaining space, and then adding an eighth-pint would fill half the space again. This would always be the case – each drink is half the size of the previous, and would fill half the remaining space in the glass. We'll never actually go over the full glass – the infinitely many drinks poured together would never come to more than two pints.

Will it ever reach two pints? If we stop somewhere along the line – after a thousand mathematicians, say – we'd have an incredibly small but non-zero gap at the top of the drink. But what if we carry on to infinity? Greek philosopher Zeno of Elea (c. 490–430 BCE) considered this a paradox, and wondered how we could possibly find the sum of infinitely many things.

Mathematicians often tread carefully around infinity – but in this case, they're confident to state that the exact value of the sum of the infinitely many drinks is 2. We call this the limit of the sequence of sums – while in practice you can't perform infinitely many additions, this is the value we'd expect it to eventually reach. This means the bartender can pull two pints, place them on the bar and tell the mathematicians they should know their limits!

THE SUM OF AN INFINITE SEQUENCE

How can we prove that an infinite sequence of beers, each half the amount of the previous one, adds up to exactly 2 pints? We know it'll never go above 2 – but is it less than 2? If you pick a number that's very close, like 1.9999, you could walk along the queue adding drinks together to get a total larger than 1.9999 – 15 mathematicians would be enough; 30 mathematicians will get us past 1.999999999. Since this would be possible for any value you picked, no matter how close to 2 it gets, we consider the value to be exactly 2.

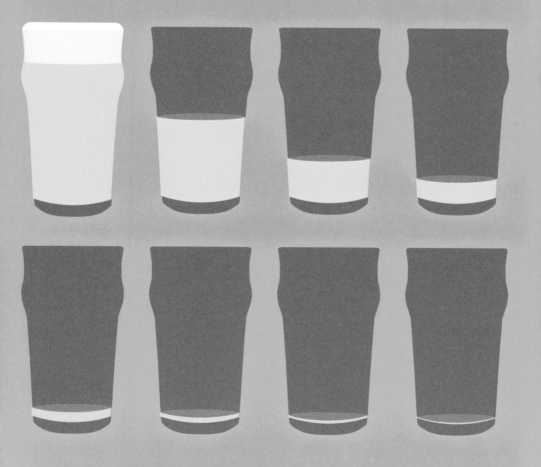

What happens when you plug something back into itself?

⟶ **If it's electrical, probably something bad! But in mathematics, the term 'plug in' refers to the inputs of a function, and feeding the output of a function back in produces a system that we can study to understand ongoing processes in the real world.**

Functions can describe how to manipulate numbers or other objects, but they can also be used to model the motion and interaction of objects in the real world (for a more detailed look at mathematical modelling, see Chapter 7). Such processes are often ongoing – the interaction between molecules, or the motion of planets in space, is continuous and changes over time.

In order to study systems like this, called dynamical systems, we consider a simple function that describes the process at one point in time, and repeatedly apply the same function to the output from the previous application. For example, we could model the population of animals in an area by creating a simple function incorporating the birth rate and death rate: $P_{n+1} = (b - d)P_n$.

Here, the population at time $n + 1$ is found by multiplying the population at a previous time n by the difference in the birth and death rates. Applying this function over and over will let us track how the population changes, and varying the rates and initial population could help us understand when systems like this are stable and when populations are likely to die out, or grow out of control.

Dynamical systems can also be used to study the motion of a physical object, like a planet orbiting in space, whose speed and direction of motion at a given point in time are determined by its current momentum and the gravitational pull of the planets around it.

Mathematicians study such systems to find out where the fixed points are – values for which the output from the function is the same as the value you put in. For example, if the function is doubling, zero will be a fixed point; but any other value – including points very close to zero – will change when the function is applied. This tells us something about when the system is stable and the kind of behaviour we'd expect to see in the long term.

FIXED POINTS

If we're modelling the position of a ball on a surface, both the very top of a hill and the bottom of a valley are fixed points – if I place a ball exactly in either of those places, it won't move. If I move the ball on the hill very slightly, its position will quickly change as it rolls down the slope, so the top of the hill is called a **repelling** fixed point. In the valley, if the ball is moved it will roll back to its original position, so the bottom of the valley is called an **attracting** fixed point.

How can we visualise infinite complexity?

⟶ **While infinitely complex structures can't be physically built in practice, mathematical abstraction allows us to construct theoretical infinitely detailed shapes called fractals, which have fascinating properties.**

Imagine I take an equilateral triangle, split it into four smaller triangles and remove the middle one. This is a simple procedure, but the result is a shape made from three smaller copies of the original triangle I started with. As with dynamical systems, fractals are often formed by repeating the same simple steps over and over – so we can repeat this process infinitely many times.

Doing so will result in a shape called the Sierpiński triangle. While in practice, trying to make such a triangle would run up against several real-world problems – for one, it would take an infinitely long time to make, and for another, you'd eventually need to remove triangular sections smaller than a single atom – but we can imagine the result as an abstract structure.

This particular fractal crops up in other places too, such as Pascal's triangle, which is made by starting with a 1 in the first row (imagining zeroes either side) and writing a number in the gap below each pair that's the sum of the two numbers above. If you colour in only the even numbers in this triangle, the result is a Sierpiński triangle.

Fractals can also arise as the result of a different type of iteration, closer to a dynamical system. For example, if we pick one of the three corners of a triangle at random, then repeat the triangle, each time moving halfway between our current position and the new corner we picked, the points we visit will only ever be points within the Sierpiński triangle. Fractals also arise as the visualisations of parameter spaces and basins of attraction in dynamical systems.

THE SIERPIŃSKI TRIANGLE

The Sierpiński triangle, named after Polish mathematician Wacław Sierpiński, has some interesting properties. For example, the total area of triangles removed from the original triangle during the repeating process that forms the fractal will add up to the same area as the original triangle itself – so the resulting fractal has zero area.

Consider also the length of the outline of the shape, including the edges of any internal holes. Since this increases each time a triangle is divided, the outline of the shape in the infinite limit is infinitely long. So, we would need zero paint to colour in the fractal, but drawing its outside edges would use up infinitely many pencils.

Can we always predict the future?

⟶ Studying dynamical systems allows us to observe how they evolve over time – and if the system is simple enough, or we can model it in enough detail, theoretically we can always predict what will happen. But the mathematical concept of chaos means that's not the whole story...

Dynamical systems are deterministic – this means that whatever the current state of the system is, we can use the definition of the function to run time forwards and find out what will happen in the future. But some systems exhibit a property called chaos, which is a word often used to describe unpredictable behaviour.

Mathematically, chaos doesn't mean something is hard to predict. Given a specific input, we can find the precise output. But in chaotic systems, we have a property called sensitivity to initial conditions – if we make a small change to the value of the input, this might result in a large change to the outcome. Sometimes known as the butterfly effect, this highlights how a simple system can have underlying patterns and feedback loops which give unpredictable results when we change the input.

This contrasts with our notion of continuity (see page 90), where making small changes to

the input varies the output only slightly; but since we're applying the function repeatedly, and looking hundreds or thousands of iterations in the future, small changes to the input can build up and even continuous functions can exhibit chaotic behaviour.

The classic example of a chaotic system is a double pendulum – an arm hinged in two places, which can swing around freely. Setting off the pendulum from one starting position, with a push of a given speed in a given direction, will result in very different behaviour than you'll see if you try again from a very similar position and initial push.

Real-world systems modelled by mathematicians, including the climate and weather, often demonstrate chaotic behaviour due to the high degree of complexity present in the system. Chaos has also been observed in human heartbeat irregularities, the behaviour of magnets in magnetic fields, and complex artificial systems like the stock market.

CHAOS AND THE LOGISTIC MAP

The logistic map, which is used to model population dynamics, is given by the map $x_{n+1} = ax_n(1 - x_n)$. Despite its simple definition, it exhibits chaotic behaviour, which can be seen in this diagram showing how the fixed points (see page 94) and periodic points (where the value bounces around between a set of points) for the map change for increasing values of a. The behaviour is simple for smaller values of a, but as a increases we see the population vary between two possible sizes, before the behaviour descends into chaos.

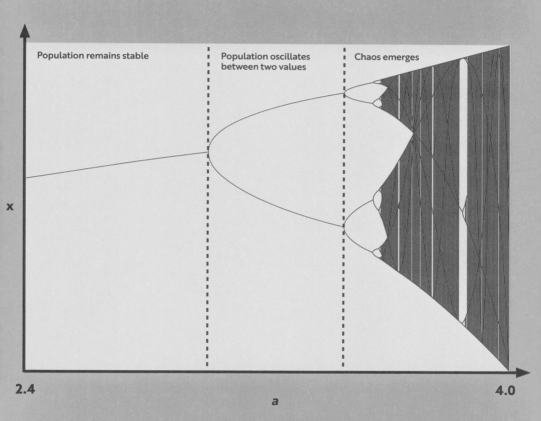

Population remains stable

Population oscillates between two values

Chaos emerges

x

2.4

4.0

a

How can you win a million dollars with pure mathematics?

⟶ Making money with maths is usually associated with applied mathematics, which helps us solve industrial problems and build lucrative technologies. But thanks to the Clay Mathematics Institute, there's a way for pure maths – with no obvious real-world applications – to pay big too.

Plenty of research institutions fund research into pure mathematics – not least because purely abstract thinking can often lead to insights which later pay off with useful applications, but also because there are some questions we just need to know the answer to in order to understand the universe better.

In 2000, the Clay Mathematics Institute in the United States chose seven problems that were the current outstanding major questions that mathematics needed answering. Some of them are in applied mathematics, like the Navier–Stokes equations, which concern fluid dynamics (see page 134). Others overlap with other fields like computer science, including the P vs NP question, while yet others are purely mathematical. Each question was accompanied by a cash prize of $1 million, awarded to whoever managed to answer the question first. The hope was that this would motivate us to answer these questions and unlock new fields of mathematics.

One of the seven problems is the Riemann hypothesis – a problem so old it was also included on a similar list of open problems posed by mathematician David Hilbert 100 years earlier – which concerns a particular function, called the Riemann zeta function. A solution to this problem would allow us to understand the mathematical mystery of prime numbers (see page 20), which, despite being a crucial concept in number theory, still holds a lot of mystery.

The zeta function is defined on the complex plane (see page 26), taking in a complex number and returning a numerical value. Mathematicians are often interested in the places where a function outputs zero. For the zeta function, these zeroes seem to occur randomly along the vertical line at the value ½, and their pattern is connected to the distribution of primes. The hypothesis states that all of these zeroes lie exactly on the line. This is known to be true for the first 10^{13} zeroes – but nobody has won the million dollars yet!

THE RIEMANN HYPOTHESIS

Since the zeta function takes a complex number as an input, the true plot is four-dimensional – but this slice through the plot shows the parts most interesting to mathematicians: the zeroes of the function. Inputting a negative even number to the zeta function always gives zero – these are called the 'trivial zeroes' – and all other zeroes are known to lie in the 'critical strip', between 0 and 1 on the horizontal axis. The question is, are they all exactly on the line at ½? Mathematicians have tried to narrow this down, but a proof remains elusive.

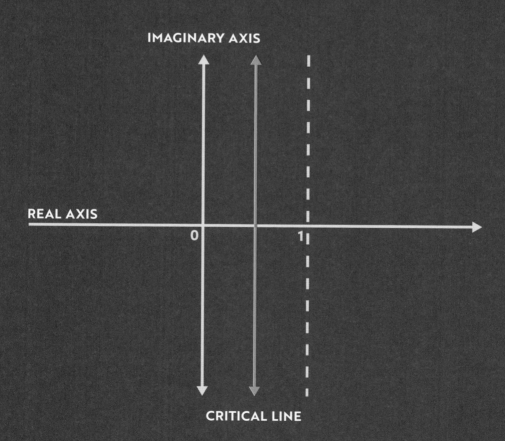

IMAGINARY AXIS

REAL AXIS

0

1

CRITICAL LINE

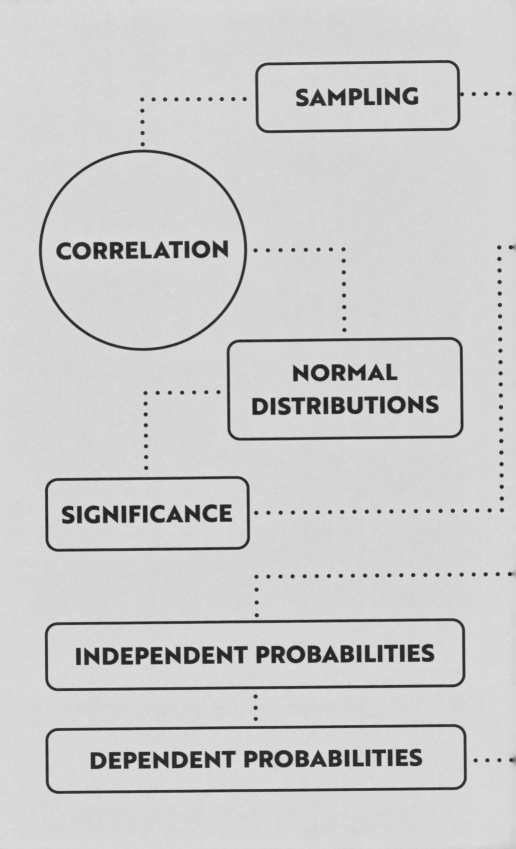

CHAPTER 6

PROBABILITY AND STATISTICS

HYPOTHESIS TESTING

BAYES' THEOREM

INTRODUCTION

A branch of mathematics that's often considered separately, **STATISTICS** is an important discipline which allows us to analyse data, make predictions and understand outcomes – and includes the powerful tool of probability. Statistics are invaluable in scientific research, including medicine and social sciences, as well as mathematical modelling and political science.

Surveys are one of the most obvious ways people interface with statistics, and they allow us to gauge the opinions of a much larger group, or a whole population, by asking only a small number of people. The most important thing when sending out a survey – or undertaking any kind of statistical **SAMPLING** – is to make sure your sample is representative of the population as a whole.

It's great to see the results of a survey pointing you towards a conclusion, especially if it's one you set out to prove in the first place. But mathematicians are careful not to draw conclusions without being mathematically certain. The concept of **SIGNIFICANCE** is a useful way to measure if what you're seeing is actually a meaningful result, or just random fluctuations in the data.

And even when you do see a relationship between two things – for example, it's been shown that people tend to spend more money in shops when the weather is cold than when it's hot – it's important not to attribute this **CORRELATION** to an actual causal link. Understanding the meaning behind the statistics you're seeing – for instance, maybe Christmas shopping is a factor in this phenomenon, and it's not just that people spend less when it's hot out – allows you to avoid making assumptions.

An important tool in statistics is the **NORMAL DISTRIBUTION** – a standard 'bell curve' of values which is observed in many real-world situations, like people's heights or incomes, or the total you get when rolling multiple dice. Values around the middle of the range tend to come up more often than extreme values, and this allows us to test whether statistical phenomena are significant, and make predictions about how likely events are.

PROBABILITY is a key aspect of statistics, since often it's used to make predictions about how likely events are to occur, as in weather forecasting. **INDEPENDENT EVENTS** aren't influenced by each other – for example, if I flip a coin twice, the chances of it coming up heads the second time don't depend on what happened the first time, but if I grab a pair of socks at random from a drawer filled with different-coloured socks, the chances of them being a particular colour change depending on what colour socks I grabbed yesterday.

When dealing with interactions between different probabilities, **BAYES' THEOREM** allows us to combine the chances of different events in a way that takes into account the dependence between them. If I pulled red socks from my drawer yesterday, the chance that I get red socks again today is lower, and Bayes' theorem allows us to quantify this probability in all kinds of situations – including in finance, in courtrooms and in decision analysis.

Whatever situation you're in, the chances are good that probability and statistics will have some use, and understanding these key concepts can help you to interpret what you're seeing in the news, and make good decisions when deciding whether to take a gamble.

PROBABILITY AND STATISTICS MAP

CONFOUNDING FACTORS
A third variable that influences two variables which are correlated. You might find that more people carry umbrellas when their shoes are wet – the confounding factor is that it's raining!

RANDOM SAMPLE
A group chosen from a larger population in such a way that every member of the larger population has an equal chance of being chosen.

CORRELATION
A statistical relationship between two sets of data – but not necessarily a causal relationship!

SAMPLING
Methods by which a representative group is selected for a survey or other research. A big challenge in statistics is to choose a group to study which is representative of the whole cohort.

STATISTICS
The area of mathematics dealing with the collection, analysis and interpretation of data. Statistics allows us to make observations about a small subset of a population and make inferences about the whole group based on our findings.

NORMAL DISTRIBUTION
A probability distribution – plotted as a bell-shaped curve – with most results occurring somewhere in the middle and only a few out towards the edges. Many random variables have a normal distribution.

SIGNIFICANCE
An observation is statistically significant when we can determine that it is extremely unlikely to have happened due to chance, and is indeed a genuine effect.

PROBABILITY DISTRIBUTION
A mathematical function that represents the probability of each different possible outcome of an event occurring.

STATISTICS

PROBABILITY

How likely an event is to occur, expressed as a value between 0% and 100%. If we did something 100 times, how many times would we expect to see a particular outcome?

PROBABILITY

CENTRAL LIMIT THEOREM

Proves that if we take sufficiently many samples from a population, the averages of those samples follow a normal distribution, meaning that statisticians can apply statistical techniques based on the normal distribution in many situations, even when the underlying dataset is not normally distributed.

INDEPENDENT EVENTS

Some probabilities depend on each other, as a given outcome in one case may affect the chances of another. Independent events – like separate coin flips – don't affect each other's probabilities.

RANDOM VARIABLE

A quantity that doesn't have one specific value but instead depends on the outcome of a random event, such as rolling a dice, or choosing a person from a group and measuring their height.

DEPENDENT EVENTS

If two events are not independent, then the probability of the second happening is conditional on whether or not the first event happens.

BAYES' THEOREM

Explains how the probability of an event happening is affected by other events. What are the chances of A happening, given that B has happened, and is it the same as the probability of B happening, given that A has happened?

How do you find out what people who dislike surveys think?

⟶ Even if you hate doing surveys, thanks to clever applications of statistical techniques developed in the mid-20th century, researchers can find out what you – or people like you – think by asking carefully chosen samples of people.

Finding out what people think has historically been an enormous challenge for governments, organisations and companies. Surveying everybody is hugely expensive and time-consuming, but accurate predictions are needed to make decisions on where to invest resources, what to produce or how to follow public opinion.

Early work on sampling techniques was based on a desire by pollsters such as George Gallup to predict election results accurately, and to target campaigning to the areas where it would bear most fruit in the late stages of an electoral race. Gallup used the analogy of a cook tasting a pan of soup to explain how his organisation conducted surveys: when you are making soup, and you want to know if it needs more seasoning, instead of just tasting a spoonful from the top, you stir the pan first.

When you want to know public opinion, you need to ask a sample of people who represent the population as a whole. Some surveys, such as censuses, ask just about everyone in a country, and this data can then be used to help make future surveys more representative. Statisticians use census data when designing studies so that their smaller samples are chosen to represent different distinct groups, weighted according to how prevalent they are in the overall population. This is known as stratified sampling.

One big advantage of this technique is that each group or stratum can then be surveyed in an appropriate way to their demographic. For example, in a survey stratified according to different age groups, surveyors might use traditional landline telephone or door-knocking surveys to reach pensioners, while using mobile phones, street surveys or social media to seek out the opinions of a younger demographic. So don't worry if you've never been asked your opinions for an opinion poll. Statisticians have worked very hard to make sure they asked someone quite like you!

SAMPLING

In this population of 100 people (below), 50% are happy, 30% are neither happy nor sad, and 20% are sad. A well-designed survey using random sampling techniques should lead to a sample of 10 people (above) containing approximately five happy people, three neutral people and two sad people. The best sampling methods are designed to make sure that everyone has an equal chance that their views are heard. There is no perfect method of sampling, but by careful design, researchers can minimise the effects of bias.

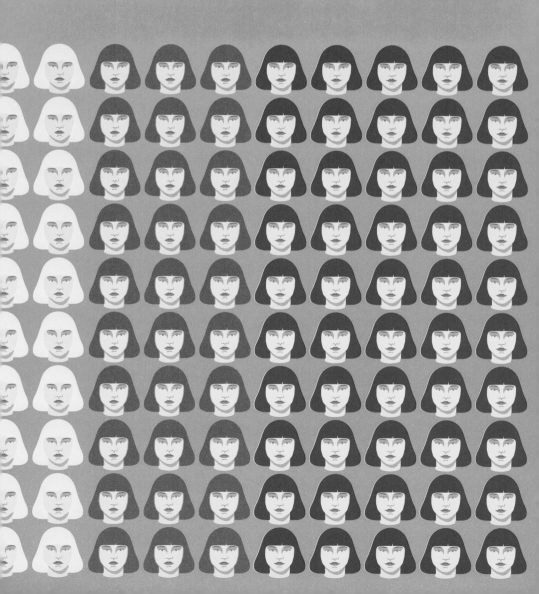

Do Nicolas Cage films cause drownings?

⟶ **Plotting drownings on the same axes as the number of Nicolas Cage films from 1999 to 2009 shows a remarkably close correlation. However, correlation does not mean that one causes the other, so it's probably safe to let Nicolas Cage carry on making films.**

A common misconception about statistics is the idea that two variables being correlated means that one causes the other. To unpack this, we need to understand what it means for two variables to be correlated. Correlation is a statistical relationship between two sets of data. At its simplest level, we might decide whether two variables are correlated by drawing a scatter plot and seeing whether a trend line or line of best fit can be drawn.

For example, we could measure the height and shoe size of a group of adults to see whether taller people tend to have bigger feet. Once we have made a scatter plot of our data, we can draw a line of best fit to represent any trends in the data. For height and shoe size, there is a general trend that the average shoe size for taller people is higher than the average for shorter people. This is known as a positive correlation.

Negative correlations occur when the trend line slopes down rather than up, so that as one variable increases the other decreases. If we plot data for the number of ice creams and hot drinks sold, we'd expect the variables to be negatively correlated, since on hot days it's likely people will buy ice cream whereas on cold days they'll buy hot drinks. So as hot drink sales increase, ice cream sales decrease.

Just because two variables are correlated doesn't mean one causes the other. They could have the same underlying cause, or it could just be a coincidence. Nicolas Cage films being closely correlated with drownings is one of many examples collected by Tyler Vigen on the *Spurious Correlations* website to illustrate that correlation alone is not enough to prove a causal link. So whenever we find variables that correlate, it's important to consider all the facts before jumping to the conclusion that one causes the other.

CORRELATION

If we gather data on the number of people being treated for sunburn and the number of ice creams sold, there is a positive correlation – as the number of ice creams sold increases, the number of sunburn victims goes up. It's not because eating ice cream causes sunburn, though – there is a common cause of both ice cream consumption and sunburn: sunny days.

What does it mean to be normal?

⟶ **In statistics, 'normal' doesn't mean just regular or ordinary. A 'normal distribution' is the classic 'bell curve' pattern that appears when plotting many different types of data – statistically speaking, anything that follows this pattern could be said to be normal.**

A probability distribution is a function that represents the probability of each possible outcome of an event occurring. Imagine flipping a fair coin 10 times and recording the number of heads. This is a discrete probability distribution, where each of the outcomes is a specific value. The probabilities can be represented using a bar chart. In this case, the most likely outcome is five heads, but we could get any whole number from zero to 10.

Many examples of data in the real world are continuous rather than discrete – that is, they can take any real-numbered value. The distributions we use to make predictions about continuous data are represented by smooth curves rather than distinct bars, and the area under the curve between two values tells us the probability that an outcome lies in that range.

The normal distribution is a continuous probability distribution that provides a good model for many real-world situations. Its distinctive shape – known as the 'bell curve' – has a bulge in the middle and tails off symmetrically on either side. If you plotted the heights of every adult living in a particular town you would find many of average height, but only a few who are very tall or very short.

The normal distribution is hugely important in statistics because of the central limit theorem, which proves that if we take sufficiently many samples from a population, the averages of those samples follow a normal distribution. This means that statisticians can apply statistical techniques based on the normal distribution in many situations, even when the underlying dataset is not normally distributed.

Normal distributions are expressed in terms of two parameters: the mean or average value, which gives the position of the centre of the curve; and the standard deviation, which is a measure of how spread out the data is from the mean. Approximately 68% of a normally distributed data set is within one standard deviation of the mean, and approximately 95% is within two standard deviations. So to decide whether you are normal or an outlier, you just need to know how many standard deviations you are away from the mean.

NORMAL DISTRIBUTIONS

The two normal distributions shown in the graph below represent the heights of two groups of athletes. From the shape of the distributions we can deduce that, on average, the male athletes are taller than the female athletes, because the axis of symmetry for the male distribution is further to the right. We can also deduce that the female athletes are more closely matched in height than the male athletes, since the male distribution is flatter, which means the male athletes have a wider range of different heights.

How do you impress a statistician?

➞ **If you want to impress a statistician, you will need to convince them that your claims are statistically significant, so that they know it's unlikely your results happened purely by chance.**

In many areas of study, researchers need a way to test whether their theories are supported by experimental results. One statistical method for doing this is known as hypothesis testing.

The first step in a hypothesis test is to come up with the 'null' hypothesis, often written H_0. The null hypothesis is based on the assumption that the statement being tested is false – that there is no underlying difference between two probability distributions, and any observed difference is due solely to chance.

For example, if a new restaurant, Anna's Amazing Pizza, claims that it delivers faster than its competitor, Tony's Tastiest Pizza, a null hypothesis might be that the two average delivery times are equal. The null hypothesis is tested against an alternative hypothesis called H_1. Our H_1 is that Anna's Amazing Pizza has a faster average delivery time. The restaurant may produce data that shows a faster average delivery time, but this isn't sufficient to support its claim; it's possible that it just happened to get lucky with the data points it chose. A hypothesis test allows us to quantify how lucky it would need to be to get those results.

To test the hypothesis, we need to choose a significance level. This is the threshold at which it's unlikely that the null hypothesis is true, commonly chosen to be 5% or 1%. Now we carry out the test. First we model the probability distribution of the delivery time data from Tony's Tastiest Pizza (see page 112 for more about probability distributions). Then we collect data for Anna's Amazing Pizza, work out its average delivery time and see how it compares. If, according to our model, there's a less than 5% chance of Anna's Amazing Pizza's average occurring, then we reject the null hypothesis and conclude that Anna's Amazing Pizza is faster.

So, if you want to impress a statistician, show them that the probability that you just got lucky when collecting your data is really small, so your results are statistically significant.

HYPOTHESIS TESTING

Hypothesis testing is similar to a jury trial in a courtroom. The null hypothesis is the assumption that the defendant is innocent. The jury do not find the defendant 'guilty' unless there is sufficient evidence to reject the hypothesis of innocence. However, finding the defendant 'not guilty' does not necessarily mean they are innocent – just that there wasn't sufficient evidence to convict them. This is why researchers talk about 'failing to reject the null hypothesis' rather than 'accepting the null hypothesis'.

If you flip 10 heads in a row, is the next flip more likely to be tails?

⟶ **Flipping 10 heads in a row with a fair coin has a less than 1 in 1,000 chance of happening, but that doesn't make the next flip more likely to be tails. The chance is 50-50 whether it's the first flip or the 11th.**

When two events happen successively, either the first affects the chances of the second, or the two are unrelated. In probability theory, this concept is called independence. Two events are independent if the probability of the second event happening is the same regardless of whether or not the first event happens.

You might think it's a bad idea to buy a lottery ticket with last week's winning numbers, because it seems highly unlikely that the same numbers will come out two weeks in a row – but they're just as likely as any other set of numbers (that is, not very likely at all). Each week's numbers are chosen by a random process that doesn't depend on previous weeks, so the two events are independent.

Dependent events occur when the probability of one event is affected by the result of another event. Imagine you have five black and five navy T-shirts. If you dress in the dark, there's a 50% chance you'll put on a black T-shirt. But the following morning, the chance of putting on a black T-shirt is only $4/9$, or about 44%. The probability of getting a black shirt on day two depends on the outcome of day one, so they are not independent events.

Knowing that events are independent is a useful tool when calculating probabilities. When considering the likelihood of two independent events both happening, we can multiply the probabilities of the individual events together. With a fair coin, each flip is independent of the previous one, so the probability of getting 10 heads in a row on a fair coin can be calculated by multiplying together 10 individual probabilities of $\frac{1}{2}$, giving a probability of $1/1024$. This is pretty unlikely – so if someone flips 10 heads in a row in front of you, it's a good idea to check that their coin isn't a double-headed penny!

INDEPENDENT PROBABILITIES

A driver is approaching three traffic lights. For each individual traffic light, the probability that it's red when the driver arrives at it is 60%, or 0.6, and the probability that it's green is 40%, or 0.4. If each traffic light were independent, the chance of getting through all three lights on green would be only 0.4 × 0.4 × 0.4 = 0.064, or just over 6%; but since traffic lights are often controlled together, the probabilities are not independent, meaning there's somewhere between a 6% and 40% chance of a 'green wave'.

How can probability catch a criminal?

⟶ **Whether you're trying to predict where a gang of bank robbers will strike next or to figure out where their lair is to catch them lying low, Bayes' theorem can narrow down the field.**

Bayes' theorem is an important rule in probability theory that explains how the chance of an event happening is affected by other events. It links the probability that A happens given that B happens and the probability that B happens given that A happens. At first glance, it might seem that these two things are the same, but as the following example shows, they aren't.

Suppose that around 1% of people have metal in their pocket when they go through an airport scanner. If the scanner is 90% accurate, it beeps 90% of the time when metal is present, but it also beeps 10% of the time when no metal is present. The probability of a beep given that someone is carrying metal is 90%, but the probability that someone is carrying metal given that there's a beep is only around 8%.

Bayes' theorem links these two probabilities, as well as the probabilities of each event happening independently of the other (see page 116). This means that if we know either probability, we can use it to work out the other. It also underpins a technique known as Bayesian inference, where statisticians develop a model of what they think a probability distribution is and update their model as more information emerges.

Bayesian inference can help catch criminals by narrowing down the location of their hideout. Suppose a crime gang has carried out a few robberies. We know they're somewhere in the city, but we don't know where. So for each street where they might be based, we make a prediction of which banks they would rob, based on information about how criminals choose their targets. This is the probability that criminals would rob each bank given that they live on a particular street. Using Bayes' theorem, we can use this to find the probability the criminals live on a street, given that they rob each bank, which lets us narrow down the search and catch the criminals before their next heist.

BAYES' THEOREM

Say 1,000 people go through a scanner. Ten people, or 1%, have something metal in their pocket. When the 990 people without metal go through the scanner, it beeps 10% of the time, so there are 99 beeps. When the 10 people with metal go through, it beeps 90% of the time, so there are nine beeps. In total, there are 108 beeps, and only nine are for people carrying metal. So the probability that someone's carrying metal, given a beep, is $\frac{9}{108}$, or approximately 8%.

	BEEP	NO BEEP	TOTAL
KEYS	9	1	10
NO KEYS	99	891	990
TOTAL	108	892	1,000

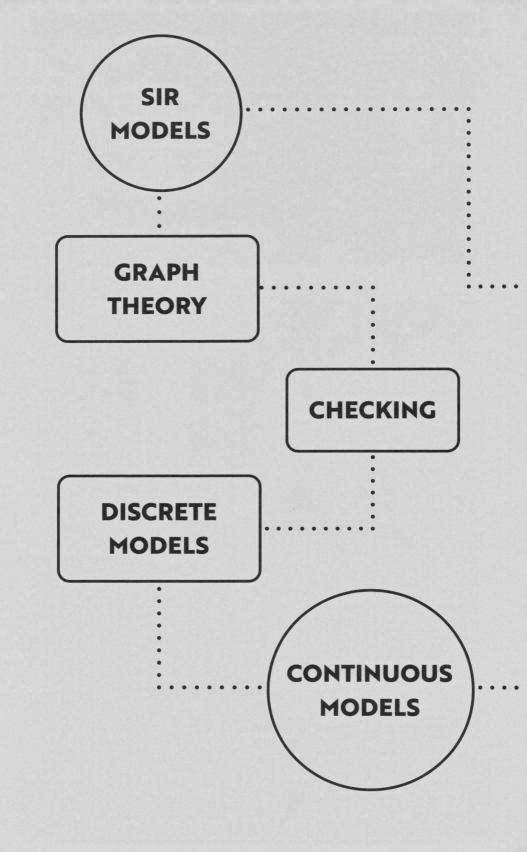

CHAPTER 7

MODELLING

ESTIMATION

SIMULATION

INTRODUCTION

MATHEMATICAL MODELLING is the process of translating real-world situations into mathematical ideals – approximations or simplifications which allow us to perform mathematical analysis and make predictions about a system and how it might change in the future.

It's a delicate balance between making a model accurate enough that it captures the real world exactly, and keeping it simple enough that the calculations can be performed quickly enough to be useful. The key to successful mathematical modelling is making the right **ASSUMPTIONS** and approximations – which aspects of the situation are most important, what might we expect them to be, and what can be ignored?

FERMI ESTIMATION is a nice example of this kind of assumption-making in practice – it involves answering a question nobody could possibly know the precise answer to, like 'How long would it take to read all the books in the Library of Congress?' In order to answer this, you might want to know how many books are in the library, and use estimates of how quickly the average person reads, and how many words there are in an average book, to figure out a rough guess at how long it would take overall.

Modelling becomes particularly important when real-world situations need immediate answers or predictions in order to manage an ongoing crisis. The COVID-19 pandemic has seen a huge number of mathematicians and epidemiologists using models to understand not just the mathematics behind how diseases spread, but how that interacts with the **CONTEXT** it's being modelled in.

One important use of mathematical modelling is to make predictions about the future. For simple questions about short timescales, it's possible to verify whether your prediction came true by just waiting long enough and making observations. Feedback from observations can be used to refine and redevelop the model as part of the **MODELLING CYCLE**.

If you want to test a model, often a good approach is **SIMULATION** – this involves generating sample data based on what you'd expect each individual or aspect of the model to do in a given situation, and running it through your model to see if the results look like what you're expecting. Simulations involve an element of probability, meaning you'll get different results each time you run them – but this can allow you to anticipate what might happen in a real situation, where you can expect a degree of randomness.

Modelling can be used for all kinds of different systems – including simple **DISCRETE MODELS**, which capture information about systems that move through a limited number of possible states in individual time steps. We'll see how modelling a social network can help us understand how internet search results are optimised.

We can also use **CONTINUOUS MODELS** for more complex, constantly changing systems, like the movement of liquids and gases, from simply modelling the flow inside a single pipe to optimise its shape, through to enormous interlinked systems like weather. Our understanding of this kind of flow allows us to model other situations too, like the motion of crowds within buildings.

MODELLING MAP

MATHEMATICAL MODELLING

The process of describing a real-world situation or system using mathematics, in order to understand and predict its behaviour. Mathematical modelling is crucial to weather prediction, public health, product design and economic decision making.

ASSUMPTIONS

The choices we make about how to model something, which affect how accurate the model is, and how easy it is to use.

THE MODELLING CYCLE

The iterative process of creating a model, taking into account the context and your assumptions, testing it, and feeding the results back into the model to improve it.

MODELLING

ESTIMATION

The process of approximating values based on limited data. If we wanted to model a queue, we might need to estimate the rates at which customers arrive and get served, perhaps by observing the queue for a period of time.

FERMI PROBLEMS

Designed to teach estimation, these problems use unanswerable questions to prompt back-of-the-envelope calculations. They can generate useful discussion, and reasonable values can be extrapolated even in the absence of concrete data.

SIMULATION

CONTEXT
The external setting from which the model arises and into which its predictions must be placed. A model is a simplification of this context, but it's crucial to consider how simplifying assumptions affects the validity of findings and how those findings relate back to the real world.

DISCRETE MODELS
Used to model systems which have limited number of possible states, changing in individual time steps. Discrete models can be applied to networks like those on social media, which can be represented using graphs.

SIMULATION
A simulation imitates a real-world system over time based on the abstract version of reality given by a mathematical model. While a model looks at the system as a whole, a simulation plays out a particular instance or time period. A simulation incorporates randomness, and mathematicians might run a simulation many times to see a range of possible outcomes.

CONTINUOUS MODELS
Used for more complex, constantly changing systems, and expressed as a function of time. Continuous models can be applied to population dynamics, by incorporating birth and death rates, or fluid dynamics (the movement of liquids and gases).

SIR MODELS
Used in modelling pandemics like COVID-19, these track the numbers of Susceptible, Immune and Recovering patients for a particular disease, to predict spread.

How many hairs are there on a bear?

⟶ This is a classic example of a Fermi problem – a question that's really hard to answer precisely, but we can estimate an answer that's 'good enough'. Estimation, approximation and answers that are 'good enough' are at the heart of mathematical modelling.

Many aspects of the natural world and human activity manifest as complicated systems we would like to ask questions about. What will the weather be like tomorrow? What measures are needed to ensure the survival of a population of deer? How can we get a loaf of bread to your local shop when you want to buy one? Such systems have many complicating factors which mean they cannot be analysed in full detail.

A mathematical model can help. This is a simplified version of a scenario that uses assumptions and approximations to capture the essential aspects of the original context while being simple enough to analyse using mathematical and statistical techniques. Statistician George Box said, 'All models are wrong, but some are useful.' That is, models are always 'wrong' – a simplification of reality – otherwise we wouldn't be able to analyse them. But some models, where the simplification is done well, enable us to make 'useful' predictions.

The art of modelling is in making the right assumptions and approximations to produce a 'wrong, but useful' model. Physicist Enrico Fermi had a particular talent for approximations. He dropped some pieces of paper at the first nuclear weapon detonation in New Mexico in 1945. Based on how they fell, he estimated the blast as equivalent to 10 kilotons of TNT. This was close to the actual figure of 21 kilotons, and Fermi's ability to quickly produce a simple, 'good enough' estimate from very little data led to the naming of Fermi problems – a type of estimation question designed to teach approximation techniques, of which 'How many hairs are there on a bear?' is a classic example.

Sometimes a model creates predictions that are so far from reality that they are not useful and we must revisit our assumptions and approximations. This is why modelling is a cycle – we start simple, then refine to take account of more complexity as needed.

THE MODELLING CYCLE

The mathematical modelling cycle illustrates the process of modelling. A model is a simplified version that captures the key aspects of a scenario. Questions about the model are answered using mathematical techniques. The solutions are checked against data to see if they make sense; for example, do they make accurate predictions? The model may then need to be refined and solved again. Finally, it is important to communicate findings from modelling in the original context of the scenario.

SCENARIO

MATHEMATICAL MODELLING CYCLE

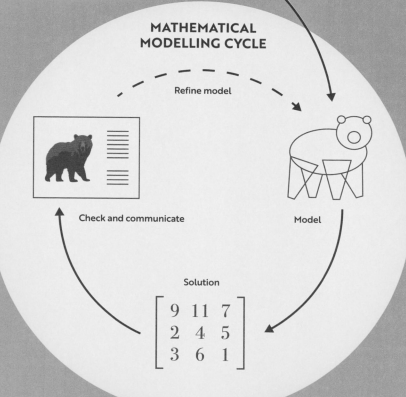

Refine model

Check and communicate

Model

Solution

$$\begin{bmatrix} 9 & 11 & 7 \\ 2 & 4 & 5 \\ 3 & 6 & 1 \end{bmatrix}$$

How can you predict a pandemic?

⟶ **There are many approaches to modelling disease outbreaks and offering advice on policy response. This is a good example of a situation where mathematical modelling must work in close relationship with a fast-developing problem context.**

A simple model of a disease outbreak might assign members of a population into groups: those who are susceptible (S) to becoming infected, those who are currently infected (I) and those who have recovered (R) from infection and are now immune. This so-called SIR model would include rates at which people move between these groups based on assumptions about how likely it is that someone might become infected and how long it might take for an infected person to recover.

It is vital that such a model is deeply embedded in its original context. Findings must be translated to the context so that those making policy decisions, who may not follow the mathematical detail, can make best use of the analysis. Also, the context may be producing rapidly evolving data. This might call the underlying assumptions and approximations into question, particularly if the model predictions are not seen to match the developing situation.

If predictions do not match reality as the outbreak progresses, and tweaks to the model don't help, it may be that a more complicated model is needed. Perhaps data on transmission reveals that people aren't infectious for as long as they are infected. Perhaps people don't gain immunity when they recover, or that immunity wanes over time. Perhaps the worst happens and the model needs to incorporate people dying from the disease. Perhaps the timescale is long enough that population change is important – can new babies be born already infected or immune? If a vaccine is available, a group of vaccinated people would be introduced.

It might also be necessary to think beyond the whole population level. How a disease spreads might vary in different contexts or based on behaviour of different demographic groups. Simulation approaches can introduce random variation into models.

It may be necessary to evaluate a scenario using several modelling approaches. Translating the findings into context and clearly communicating the underlying assumptions and resulting uncertainties is vital to good decision making.

THE SIR MODEL

The SIR model captures a basic representation of a disease outbreak by tracking changes between three states – susceptible, infected and recovered. At the start, everyone is susceptible and there is a quick increase in infected people. As time passes, the recovered group grows, fewer people are susceptible and the infected group shrinks. Eventually, the whole population is recovered and can no longer be infected. Many outbreaks are much more complicated than this and require more sophisticated models to analyse.

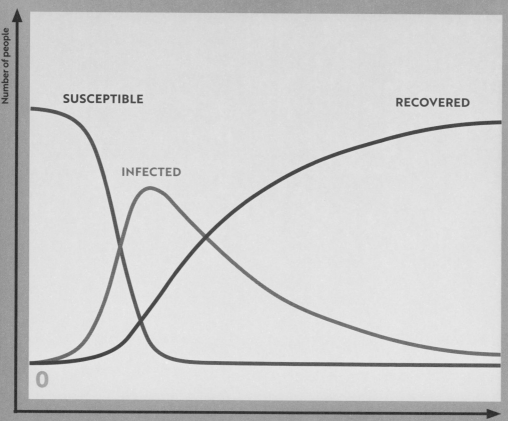

When will my cup of tea be ready to drink?

⟶ **How quickly your tea cools depends on a lot of complicated factors that are hard to take account of. However, a simple model can provide an estimate that might be good enough, and it can be checked with data.**

A hot object loses heat to the room it's in through complicated mechanisms involving radiation and convection. The air gets hotter as it absorbs the object's heat while it circulates through any doors or windows. Isaac Newton came up with a simplified model of cooling that cuts through all this by imagining a hot object cooling in a sealed room with unchanging temperature.

In this model, we don't worry about the detailed physics of how an object loses heat, but we do need to think about overall changes in its temperature. If we leave a cup of tea in a room, it will get colder. But it won't cool forever; you won't come back later and find a frozen cup of tea in a 20°C (68°F) room. It's reasonable to think that if you leave it for long enough it will match the room temperature.

The way this is expressed in the model is that the rate at which the object cools is in proportion to the difference between its temperature and the room temperature. This means a hotter object in a cold room will cool more quickly than a warm object; the same object in a colder room will cool even more quickly. It also means that as an object's temperature gets close to the room temperature, the cooling slows down. Mathematically, the model sets up a situation where the temperature of an object decreases exponentially towards the room temperature but never actually reaches it. Of course, this doesn't match reality – part of the simplification is deciding at some point that the model's temperature prediction is close enough to room temperature to say that cooling has finished.

A different model, with different assumptions, might give quite a different prediction. It is important to use data, where we can, to validate a model – to verify whether it makes sensible predictions. Here, we can do this by sticking a thermometer in a cup of tea.

DEVISING A MODEL

I put a clean thermometer in a freshly brewed cup of tea and it read 68°C (154°F). Six minutes later, it read 61°C (142°F). Using Newton's law of cooling, I estimated the rate of temperature decrease and made a prediction that the tea would reach 50°C (122°F) after 18 minutes. After 18 minutes, I measured the temperature again and found my prediction was correct. It's a model you can quickly check with real data, and it delivers a nice drink at the end!

Who should I connect with on social media?

→ Many situations can be modelled using techniques such as graph theory. Who you choose to follow on social media is up to you, but a recommendation could be made by examining the network as a graph.

We can represent a social network by drawing a graph, marking each user as a node and using arrows to connect them to all the other users they follow (see page 36).

This kind of representation is called a discrete model, because it can only be in a limited number of states and changes state abruptly: here, one user either follows another or they don't – you can't half-follow someone. By contrast, a continuous model may flow gradually between states.

We could label the nodes in our graph with how many followers they have, giving us a way of seeing who is most popular on our network. If you're looking for a recommendation of who to follow, we could take a simple approach and just suggest you follow the more popular users.

But graph theory allows us to be more sophisticated than this. Imagine we observe lots of users who are interested in a topic – say, maths – all following one user in particular, and conclude that this person is an authority on maths. If we detect you are following lots of the users interested in maths, we might guess that you are interested in maths and would like to follow this popular user too.

Now imagine the popular user follows another, less popular, user. Our model has told us the popular user is an authority on maths, and they are interested in what this other person has to say. As a maths fan yourself, you might also be interested in what this other person has to say – and while their raw number of followers doesn't seem that impressive, analysing the structure of the graph shows they're probably worth a look.

The same technique can be used to rank web pages in a search, explore the meaning of documents and examine the performance of sports people. Many other situations can be modelled and analysed as graphs, including train networks, customer loyalty and atomic structures.

GRAPH THEORY

You might be more interested in what Abby has to say on social media than Beth, because Abby is followed by the super-popular user Fern, who has many followers. Rather than simply counting followers, we can give a score to each user based on how many followers they have and what scores those followers have, so more popular users pass on a higher score to the people they follow. The techniques of graph theory can help us find patterns and explore interesting dynamics in all sorts of models.

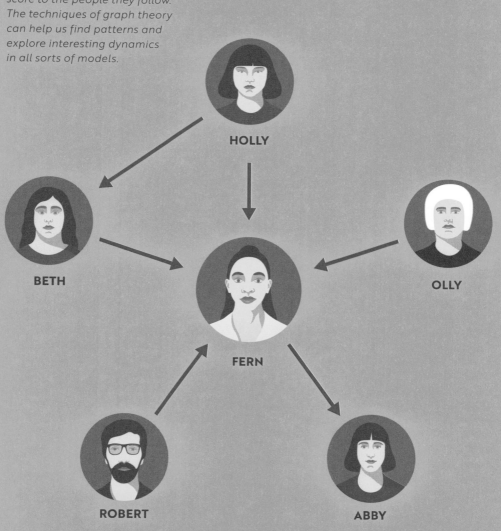

HOLLY

BETH

OLLY

FERN

ROBERT

ABBY

Why is a crowd of people like a liquid?

⟶ A crowd of people is made up of individuals making their own decisions about what to do. But by treating the crowd as a continuous flow of people, like a liquid, we can use powerful techniques like calculus to help understand how the crowd behaves.

Imagine we want to model the flow of a river. It isn't sensible to think of individual water molecules as balls bouncing around in the river channel. This is too complicated to analyse and, it turns out, unnecessary. Instead, we model liquid as a continuous volume – continuous, because mathematically speaking we can keep breaking the volume of water into smaller and smaller parts and explore how they flow around.

A mathematical modeller would represent a volume of water using a function (see page 88), because we can use techniques like calculus to explore the rate of change of functions, allowing us to explore how the water flows. We could adjust values in our equations to model different situations – for example, changing the size of the river bed and the amount of rain falling might help us explore flood risk. We might find the function generates chaos (see page 98), which appears

in our model as turbulence in the water. We could adapt our equations for other similar situations, such as water flowing into and out of a lake or the movement of liquid chemicals in pipes.

We can also use continuous models to examine systems that are not actually continuous, and the movement of a crowd is just one example. The reason we pretend these systems are continuous and behave like a volume of water is because the techniques like calculus that we can apply to functions are so powerful. Our model might help us imagine the flow of people through the corridors of a building as analogous to the flow of water in a river bed.

Functions and calculus can be used in a vast range of modelling scenarios across science, engineering and economics because very often we are interested in how things change over time. Many well-known laws of nature are expressed as continuous models.

WAVES

Oceans contain perhaps the most obvious form of waves, which are useful to understand when studying flood risk, safely positioning off-shore wind farms and designing ships. But there are lots of other waves in physics. Sound moves as a wave through substances, so understanding waves is helpful when assisting people with hearing impairments, reducing the noise caused by aeroplanes and examining shock waves from earthquakes. Light also moves as a wave, so the wave equation is also applicable in quantum mechanics.

Which queue should I join?

——▶ **The simple answer is to join the shortest queue. But this will not always be the best choice – lots of factors can affect how a queue behaves, and another queue might be moving faster. Mathematicians can use simulations to explore these dynamics.**

When you think of a queue, you might think of a line of people in a supermarket, cars at a traffic light or orders being placed in a restaurant. These are difficult systems to manage, because it can be hard to predict demand. If on average one person arrives per minute and someone has just arrived, it doesn't mean it's going to be exactly a minute until the next person arrives. The probability of someone joining the queue in the next few moments is the same no matter how long ago someone new joined.

And there are more complicated aspects to queuing than this. For example, if a queue in a shop gets to a certain length, people might be less likely to join it. Some might move between different queues. Depending how long people have to wait, some might leave without being served.

Different individuals will make these decisions differently, meaning a queue is ideal for simulation. Instead of making a model that looks at the system as a whole, a simulation can look at the different behaviour of individuals in the system and explore the consequences of their decisions.

Simulations are governed by probabilities, and so running a simulation a second time will come up with different results. But running a simulation many times and looking at the results as a whole can provide useful insight into a situation.

Many systems can be simulated as queues, including telephone calls in a customer contact centre, people calling a lift from different floors, and parts moving through a factory process. When you order a ride from an app, the app has a queue of passengers and a separate queue of drivers, and must match the two together. A queuing simulation can give insight into how many drivers might be needed on a particular day.

SUPPLY CHAINS

A supply chain is a network of production facilities which process raw materials into intermediate products, which are in turn used to create final products that may be shipped to consumers. In the case of 'just in time' development, the process is optimised so that production of each part is completed only when needed, operating as a complex network of queues. Predicting demand for the finished product is key to modelling what orders to place when at the earlier queues in the network. Simulations are run many times to give insight into the underlying model.

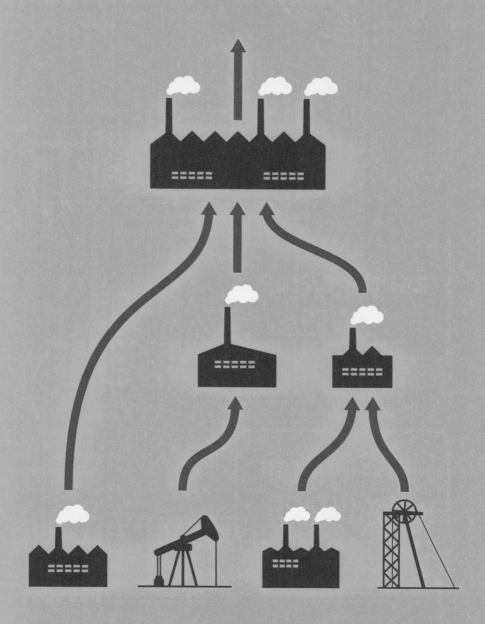

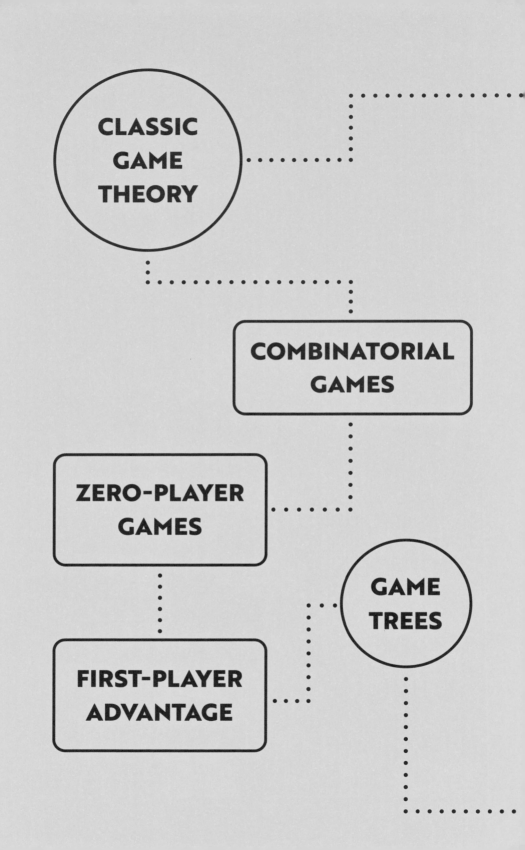

PUZZLES

CHAPTER 8

GAMES

STRATEGY

REAL-WORLD
APPLICATIONS

PAYOFFS

INTRODUCTION

Playing games is a source of joy – people enjoy a bit of competition, as well as the challenge of developing strategies and the element of chance. Many aspects of games involve mathematics; as well as the probability involved in dice rolls and card shuffles, and the necessary counting and adding to keep score, there's a lot of strategic and puzzle-based thinking which benefits from a mathematical outlook.

But it's not a new endeavour. Humans have been having fun with mathematics for longer than you might think. Recreational mathematics dates back as far as Neolithic times – and our earliest examples of mathematical writing from ancient Egypt include mathematical **PUZZLES**. Ever since, people throughout history have repeatedly shown they have an appetite for mathematical thinking as a form of play.

Strategic thinking is an important part of gameplay, and **GAME THEORY** is a branch of mathematics which involves studying decisions made by players in certain situations – whether part of a friendly game, or a more serious situation that can be modelled as a game, such as the negotiation of economic agreements by international superpowers.

We'll see how analysing competing strategies and the **PAYOFFS** in each situation can be modelled simply using a payoff matrix, and how sometimes the incentives can be unexpected – if you're given a choice of strategies, the one which leads to obvious immediate gains might not be the better choice long-term. We'll also see how these same ideas can be applied to evolutionary biology.

Game theory is considered by some to be a branch of economics, but it can also be applied to simple **COMBINATORIAL GAMES** – in which both players can see everything that's happening, and take it in turns to make sequential moves. Simple children's games like **NOUGHTS AND CROSSES** can be analysed mathematically, producing algorithms to determine the best move in a given situation.

One way to analyse a simple game is through a **GAME TREE**, which lays out all the possible moves and game states, identifying all the new situations you can put yourself in by choosing a particular set of moves. We'll see how computers can use this kind of analysis – enumerating all the possible game states, and working out which moves lead to the best outcomes – to develop strategies.

In some games, all the strategy in the world won't help you. If you introduce an aspect of probability – like dice-rolling or drawing cards from a shuffled pack – you're often relying on luck alongside skill (or, in the case of some games, not even that!). **ZERO-PLAYER GAMES**, such as **SNAKES AND LADDERS**, don't involve decision making on behalf of any player, and often involve probabilistic elements like dice which can be analysed using **MARKOV CHAINS** – ways to combine probabilities of repeated events.

While it might seem like it's all fun and games, the mathematics behind some of these pastimes can often be used for serious applications too, in modelling and predicting behaviour. Mathematicians also consider play an important part of their work – understanding the rules governing the universe, and sometimes bending the rules or trying something new to see what happens, can lead to important mathematical discoveries.

PUZZLES

A problem or toy that tests ingenuity or knowledge, including puzzles based on logic that can range from simple to very complex. Papyrus texts surviving from ancient Egyptian times include mathematical puzzles.

GAMES

A structured form of play conducted according to rules with participants in direct opposition to each other, or to the game itself. We can mathematically formalise many aspects of games, including strategies and player behaviour, information and game states. We can also model many scenarios as games, including evolution, business decision making and international diplomacy.

PLAY

ZERO-PLAYER GAMES

Games in which no choice is made by players – this can be because their decisions are made for them by dice, or because the rules, rather than players, determine how gameplay evolves.

MARKOV CHAINS

A technique used to analyse games based on probabilities where the current state of the game and the probabilities of different outcomes are used to analyse future game states. For example, in snakes and ladders, knowing where your piece is now and where the six dice rolls will take you, a Markov chain can say where you are likely to be after one or more dice rolls.

SNAKES AND LADDERS

A game in which players roll dice to determine how many spaces to move towards a goal. Some spaces propel players more quickly towards the goal (by climbing ladders) or drop them further from the goal (by sliding down snakes). The game originates in ancient India and was intended to be a lesson about karma and the power of fate and destiny to intervene in our lives, since neither player has any way to influence the outcome of the dice rolls.

GAMES

COMBINATORIAL GAMES

Turn-based games in which both players have complete information and there is no element of chance. Examples include chess and noughts and crosses.

FIRST-PLAYER ADVANTAGE

A situation in combinatorial games in which the first player, if they make certain moves, is guaranteed to win.

ZERO-SUM GAMES

In which the total amount of resource is split between the players: if one gains, the other loses. These can be used to model many situations, including in economics and business.

CLASSIC GAME THEORY

Particularly concerned with analysis of strategy in situations with uncertainty, and how players will act in a given situation depending on their options and potential outcomes.

PAYOFFS

The specific gains (or losses) a player can make by choosing a particular strategy or move in a game. In some games the payoff is in the form of points scored – but the same mathematics can model businesses in competition, where the payoff is higher profits.

NOUGHTS AND CROSSES

A simple children's game, which can be mathematically analysed. There are 19,683 ways to fill the grid with blank spaces, Xs and Os, but not all of them will occur during a real game.

GAME TREES

Used to study possible moves in a game, by mapping out all the branching possibilities and following each to see how the game could develop.

Did the ancient Egyptians play Sudoku?

→ **Sudoku was invented in the 1970s, based on Latin square puzzles that date back hundreds of years earlier. Though the ancient Egyptians may not have played Sudoku, they certainly did play around with mathematics.**

Mathematical play has a history as old as written mathematics. It comes in many forms, including puzzles, magic tricks and games. Our earliest surviving mathematical texts are papyrus from ancient Egypt and clay tablets from Mesopotamia. They show scribes learning useful mathematics – calculating areas of farmland and sharing money – but also show problems with no obvious direct application. The earliest mathematicians whose work we know were playing around with mathematics as a puzzle or game.

Mathematics as play probably goes back much further than this. We have stone balls from Neolithic Scotland which are carved with patterns showing evidence of interest in symmetries of polyhedra a millennium before the Greeks investigated them. And it pervades cultures around the world, with Chinese, Indian, Arabic and European scholars creating and sharing puzzles before the year 1000.

Collections of mathematical puzzles are evident from around 1500, with puzzle books by Luca Pacioli, Claude Gaspar Bachet and Hendrik van Etten. Mathematical puzzles and games were popular with the Victorians, created by puzzle writers such as Henry Dudeney in England and Sam Loyd in America. The mid-20th century saw a popular column on 'Mathematical Games' by Martin Gardner. The mathematical topic of game theory emerged and expanded, particularly in the latter half of the 20th century.

An 1880s puzzle craze involved the 15 puzzle: a grid of sliding numbered blocks that must be rearranged into numerical order, often seen nowadays with a picture to be unscrambled. Sam Loyd famously offered a reward for the solution of a version of the puzzle that mathematics proves cannot be solved. Later mathematical puzzle crazes included the Rubik's cube in the 1980s (see page 34) and more recently Sudoku.

It's hard to define what counts as recreational mathematics and where the line between play, puzzles and games sits. Still, it's possible to identify a type of play which is enjoyable and requires mathematical thinking or skills to engage with, and it appears this desire to play with mathematics has always been with us.

ANCIENT MATHS PUZZLES

Mesopotamian writing used cuneiform (wedge-shaped) symbols, which were pressed into wet clay tablets then baked in the hot sun. Tablet BM 85196, believed to date from between 2000 BCE and 1600 BCE, contains a collection of problems including this one: A spear of length 30 is standing upright against a wall. If the upper end slides down the wall a distance of 6, how far will the lower end move out from the wall?

6↓

30

?

What is a game?

⟶ Fire up your console, unfold a board or pop to the casino – games are activities we take part in for fun or competition. The mathematics of games can provide insights into the best way to play – and many situations can be modelled as games.

Mathematicians like to categorise different types of games, because the methods used to analyse them vary considerably. The analysis of a game where players take turns with plenty of time to think and react to the state of the game is quite different from a game where all players act at the same time.

We analyse pure strategy, turn-based games using *combinatorial game theory*. Players have time to consider the game in its current state before making their move, and the outcome of what they choose to do isn't affected by chance or hidden information. So, in theory, they can think through all the consequences of their actions and play perfectly. The challenge is understanding the game well enough to be able to think clearly through all the possibilities. Examples of combinatorial games include noughts and crosses, chess and Hex.

Classic game theory, on the other hand, deals with games where players make their moves at the same time, don't know everything about the game in play, or must deal with random elements. For example, games might have cards with hidden information or use dice to introduce probability. Games like poker, Monopoly and rock-paper-scissors fall into this category.

Because classic game theory analyses how different strategies interact, we can use it to model decision making in situations like video games, stock trading and international diplomacy. The challenge comes from having to make decisions when you don't know what unexpected elements the game might throw up. It might be that understanding probability and using this to pick a strategy leads a player to a better outcome.

For games that don't fit neatly into these categories, we can often gain some insight by making a simplified version that we can analyse. And we can sometimes get useful ideas by other methods, for example by drawing a graph or writing an algorithm to play the game, or through computer simulation.

GAME THEORY

Game theory helps us categorise and analyse different types of games. In chess, a player can carefully study the board and think through the consequences of moving their pieces, safe in the knowledge that if they choose to take an opponent's piece it will be removed from the board. Imagine instead that when a player chooses to take a piece we roll dice to see if the attempt was successful before removing the defeated piece from the board. Strategising in this game would be totally different because of the uncertainty.

Does the first player have an advantage?

➡ **In many simple games with two players taking turns, the first player can sometimes make a move that guarantees them a win. The trick is working out what move they need to make.**

⇘ Imagine two people are playing a game using a pile of sticks. Each turn, players can take one, two or three sticks from the pile. The player to take the last stick wins. You might like to play this a few times. It's a simple game, but moderately entertaining to play.

Does the first player have an advantage? Well, if we start with four sticks and I take one, two or three, then you simply take what remains and win. On the other hand, if we start with five, six or seven sticks, I can turn the tables, leaving you with four and winning myself.

This pattern also works the same with eight sticks, or 12, or any multiple of four. If I leave you 12 sticks, whatever you take I can make it eight at the end of my turn. Then whatever you take I can leave you with four and go on to win. So the first player can guarantee a win in any game where the starting number of sticks isn't a multiple of

four. They'll lose if the game starts with a multiple of four, provided the other player knows this strategy.

This game is one version of the strategy game called Nim, which may have originated in ancient China. There is a version of Nim which can be analysed using binary numbers – it is played with multiple heaps of sticks where players can remove any number of sticks from a single pile each turn. Lots of games can be analysed as equivalent to multi-pile Nim, so it's a useful game to know about.

Because both players in Nim are playing with the same sticks and aiming for the same goal, we call this game *impartial*. Games involving players moving their own pieces or having different goals are called *partisan*. We can analyse many impartial and partisan games by thinking about what options each player has at each stage in the game and what advantage that gives them.

COUNTERACTING THE FIRST-PLAYER ADVANTAGE

The game Hex is played on a grid of hexagons. Players take turns placing counters, and the winner is the player to first connect their coloured edges with a line of counters of their colour. Here, the player with blue counters has won. The first player has an advantage in Hex – to counteract this, on their first turn the second player can choose either to play normally or to take the first player's starting position as their own. This is designed to stop the first player opening too strongly.

How does a computer play noughts and crosses?

→ **A computer doesn't need to be a skilled or experienced player with lots of tricks up its sleeve. It can quickly play all possible games and decide which move to make using a clever algorithm.**

In noughts and crosses, two players, X and O, take turns to draw their symbol on a three-by-three board, aiming to be first to draw three of their symbols in a line. By convention, X goes first.

An experienced human player might tell you to start in a corner or the middle – but the computer doesn't need to be programmed with this kind of strategy. In fact, an unbeatable program could be written by someone who doesn't know how to win a game themselves. This program would simulate every possible game, starting with the nine places X could make their first move, then for each of these the eight places O could respond, and so on. There are thousands of game positions to consider, but a computer can run these in fractions of a second.

Once it's played every possible game, it scores the wins for X as +1, the losses as –1 and the draws as zero, then looks for a game that has the highest scoring outcome for X. This is more complicated than it sounds, because the players have different goals: while X would choose the highest scoring option each turn, O would play in their own best interest, choosing the option the algorithm has scored lowest. It's important for the computer to alternate goals each turn because it is looking for a sure win, not one that only works if the opponent makes a silly mistake.

A thorough analysis of noughts and crosses shows that all nine opening moves lead to games that ultimately score zero. This means if both players play perfectly, the game will always end in a draw. Searching like this can be used to analyse other games, including draughts, go and chess, and are used to make computer players for video games. The algorithm behind the search has important applications in economics and artificial intelligence.

GAME TREES

After four moves in noughts and crosses, it is X's turn. The algorithm mindlessly plays through all possible games following from the five moves X can make next, looking for the best move for each player in turn. Here, the algorithm has found a move that leads to a win for X whatever O does. We know noughts and crosses played perfectly ends in a draw, so O must have made a mistake earlier in the game.

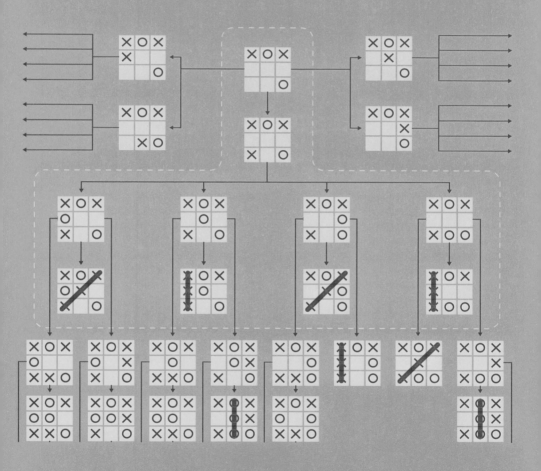

Have you ever played snakes and ladders?

⟶ **Though you might feel very invested in the outcome, if you're not making decisions that affect game play, you aren't really *playing* the game. You have never really played snakes and ladders.**

Snakes and ladders is a simple game – players take turns to roll dice, moving their counter up the board as many spaces as the number they rolled. If they finish their move on a ladder, they climb to the space at the top of the ladder. If they land on a snake, they slip down to the space at the bottom of its tail.

The question to ask is: What role are the players taking in this game? They are just acting out what the dice and the board markings tell them to do; they are not making decisions that influence the outcome. If you needed to leave the room and someone else took your go for you, the gameplay would be completely unaffected.

Snakes and ladders has its origins in ancient India, where it was created to teach the role of karma and destiny. The dice represented fate, which the players cannot influence and must simply accept. Because

of this lack of decision making, we say the people are not really playing and we call this a zero-player game.

Games of pure chance can be analysed using a technique called Markov chains. There are six outcomes from rolling a dice which lead to spaces on the board, perhaps via snakes or ladders, with known probabilities. From these spaces, we can imagine rolling the dice and moving the counter again, creating a set of probabilities for the position of the counter after roll two. And so on.

A Markov chain is used to calculate these probabilities repeatedly, to find the likelihood of being on certain spaces after a number of rolls. We might use this to ask how many rolls we expect until a player wins the game.

Markov chains can be used to analyse many chance-based board games and have wider applications in mathematical modelling in science, logistics and artificial intelligence.

MARKOV CHAINS

The probability of moving from each space to another on a snakes and ladders board can be calculated using Markov chains. For example, from 4 you have an equal chance of landing on 6, going down the snake, winning the game or overshooting the board and so not moving. You have twice the chance to get to 7, either directly or via the ladder from 5. Long-term analysis shows there's a 50% chance of reaching 'WIN' by turn five, and a 90% chance by turn 14.

How did dinosaurs play games?

⟶ In classic game theory, we model the decisions made in a game as a set of interacting strategies. But some real-world situations involve 'decisions' that aren't necessarily consciously made, and this technique can be applied to some surprising areas – including evolution.

Imagine a video game in which your character moves around a world doing battle with another player. You might choose to aggressively seek out and attack your opponent, or you might try to sneak around collecting power-ups such as new abilities or weapons. These are strategies, and we can think about how combinations of these strategies lead to different rewards, called *payoffs*, for each player.

Strategies don't just arise in situations that might be naturally thought of as games – imagine two companies selling ice cream. One strategy might be to buy quality ingredients and charge a high price; another might be to 'pile 'em high and sell 'em cheap', hoping for a greater quantity of sales.

In some games, what is gained by one player is lost by the other. In our video game battle, either one player is victorious or the other is. Such games are called *zero-sum*, because the positive gain by one player and the negative loss of the other add to zero.

In games that are not zero-sum, players can find greater collective value with some combinations of strategies than with others. If our ice cream sellers decide to compete using the quality strategy, they will split the high-paying customers between them. If one goes for quality and the other for quantity, they might both end up making more profit by targeting different markets.

We can also think about whether the gains made by each player are symmetric or not. If they are, the players are interchangeable and each gets the same reward for using a particular strategy. But if, for example, one of our video game players has spent more time in the game and knows where the power-ups are hidden, they might gain more from the stealthy strategy than their opponent would.

Modern classic game theory has its origins in the work of John von Neumann and others in the mid-20th century. Von Neumann was working in economics, but the ideas spread to applications in other areas, including biology.

PAYOFFS

Different combinations of game strategies lead to different payoffs. Suppose two dinosaurs meet over food they both want to eat. If they fight, they come away hurt and tired, with some probability of winning the food. If they don't fight, they can share the food. If a fighter meets a sharer, the fighter wins all the food as the sharer flees. We can explore how payoffs from combinations of randomly evolving strategies contribute to natural selection. For example, if two species of fighters share territory with scarce food, they would both get better payoffs by evolving a sharing approach.

IF A FIGHTER MEETS A FIGHTER...
cost to both, one wins the food

0.3 — 0.7

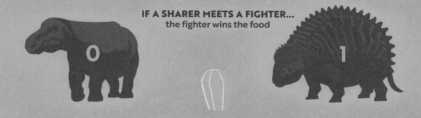

IF A SHARER MEETS A FIGHTER...
the fighter wins the food

0 — 1

IF A FIGHTER MEETS A SHARER...
the fighter wins the food

1 — 0

IF A SHARER MEETS A SHARER...
they share the food

0.5 — 0.5

FURTHER EXPLORATION

BOOKS

Cheng, E. *How to Bake π: An Edible Exploration of the Mathematics of Mathematics*. New York: Basic Books, 2016.

Cheng, E. *The Art of Logic: How to Make Sense in a World that Doesn't*. London: Profile Books, 2019.

Czerski, H. *Storm in a Teacup: The Physics of Everyday Life*. London: Bantam Press, 2016.

du Sautoy, M. *The Music of the Primes: Why an Unsolved Problem in Mathematics Matters*. London: HarperPerennial, 2003.

Eastaway, R. *Maths on the Back of an Envelope: Clever Ways to (Roughly) Calculate Anything*. London: HarperCollins, 2021.

Eastaway, R., & Wyndham, J. *How Long Is a Piece of String? More Hidden Mathematics of Everyday Life*. London: Portico, 2021.

Hope, J. *100% Proof! The Why of Maths*. UK: Percival Press, 2016.

Mason, J., Burton, L., and Stacey, K. *Thinking Mathematically*. 2nd ed. London and New York: Pearson, 2010.

Neale, V. *Closing the Gap: The Quest to Understand Prime Numbers*. Oxford: Oxford University Press, 2017.

Orlin, B. *Math with Bad Drawings: Illuminating the Ideas that Shape Our Reality*. New York: Black Dog & Leventhal, 2018.

Parker, M. *Things to Make and Do in the Fourth Dimension*. London: Penguin, 2015.

Riehl, E., Gross, B., & Harris, J. *Fat Chance: Probability from 0 to 1*. Cambridge: Cambridge University Press, 2019.

Schneps, L., & Colmez, C. *Math on Trial: How Numbers Get Used and Abused in the Courtroom*. New York: Basic Books, 2013.

Singh, S. *Fermat's Last Theorem*. London: Fourth Estate, 1997.

Strogatz, S. *The Calculus of Friendship*. Princeton: Princeton University Press, 2009.

Yates, K. *The Maths of Life and Death*. London: Quercus, 2019.

ONLINE RESOURCES

Chalkdust Magazine
chalkdustmagazine.com

Desmos
desmos.com

GeoGebra
geogebra.org

Mathigon
mathigon.org

Numberphile
youtube.com/numberphile

Plus
plus.maths.org

PODCASTS

A Problem Squared
aproblemsquared.libsyn.com

The Joy of x
quantamagazine.org/tag/the-joy-of-x

Mathematical Objects
aperiodical.com/podcasts/mathematical-objects

Relatively Prime
relprime.com

NOTES ON CONTRIBUTORS

CONSULTANT EDITOR

Katie Steckles

Katie Steckles is a mathematician based in Manchester, UK, who gives talks and workshops and writes about mathematics. She finished her PhD in 2011, and since then has talked about maths at universities, schools events, festivals, on BBC radio and TV, in books and on the internet. Katie writes regularly for the Spektrum Scilogs blog and her own blog at The Aperiodical, and has written several popular mathematics books.

ILLUSTRATOR

Robert Fiszer

An illustrator and designer based in London, Robert creates conceptual vector illustrations for books, web and advertising. His style is clean and minimalist, ensuring that the viewer is drawn directly to the essence of the image and its meaning. www.robertfiszer.com

CONTRIBUTORS

Sam Hartburn

Sam Hartburn is a freelance mathematician, author, editor and proofreader with a BSc in mathematics from York University. She has worked on more than 300 maths books and articles, spanning the spectrum from primary school to undergraduate and from academic research to recreational maths. In her spare time she writes and performs songs about maths.

Alison Kiddle

Alison Kiddle is a mathematics communicator, educator and writer from the East of England. Since studying mathematics at Cambridge University, Alison has worked as a teacher and in university outreach, created thousands of teaching resources, and led workshops and given talks about mathematics around the world for audiences of all ages.

Peter Rowlett

Peter Rowlett teaches mathematics at Sheffield Hallam University in the UK, including mathematical modelling, game theory and history of maths. He researches mathematics education with particular focus on how best to teach maths at university. He has written more than 150 articles, mostly on educational research but also including writing on history of mathematics in *Nature* and setting puzzles for *New Scientist*.

INDEX

ACKNOWLEDGEMENTS

I'd like to express my thanks to Jason Hook, who brought me on board as commissioning editor, and Jodi Simpson for her wonderful project management, guiding and nudging to keep everything on track. Thanks also to Caroline Orr for her patient and helpful copy-editing work, as well as my co-authors, whose willingness to collaborate and share their expertise has made the whole process a breeze. Final and eternal thanks go to Paul, who made cups of tea at just the right times.

Katie Steckles

UniPress Books would like to thank Robert Fiszer for his illuminating illustrations and Alex Coco for his elegant design work.